DISCARD

D0397655

Self-Therapy for the Stutterer
Fifth Edition

Speech Foundation of America

Self-Therapy for the Stutterer

Fifth Edition

MALCOLM FRASER
Director
SPEECH FOUNDATION OF AMERICA
Publication No. 12

Published by

Speech Foundation of America
P. O. Box 11749
Memphis, Tennessee 38111

Library of Congress # 84-52792
ISBN 0-933388-24-1 (Hardbound)

Not Copyrighted

Reproduction of the material in this book in whole or in part is encouraged, but in the interest of the truth it is requested that quotations be made plainly in connection with the context.

The Speech Foundation of America is a non-profit charitable organization dedicated to the prevention and treatment of stuttering.

*Dedicated to all
who seek relief from the burden
of stuttering.*

To the Reader

There are always some stutterers who are unable to get professional help and others who do not seem to be able to profit from it. There are some who prefer to be their own therapists. In this book, Malcolm Fraser, Director of the Speech Foundation of America, has attempted to provide some guidance for those who must help themselves. Knowing well from his own experience as a stutterer the difficulties of self-therapy, he outlines a series of objectives and challenges that should serve as a map for the person who is lost in the dismal swamp of stuttering and wants to find a way out.

CHARLES VANRIPER

Distinguished Professor Emeritus and formerly Head, Department of Speech Pathology and Audiology, Western Michigan University

Contents

*Use the Index (page 189) for location of instructive
information concerning all phases of the problem*

The stutterer in this book will often be referred to as "he" or "him". This is done for editorial reasons, but may be considered as fairly representative since it is estimated that there are about four times as many male stutterers as there are female.[1]

---

[1]There is less stuttering among girls than among boys. This may be attributed to the fact that girls are better organized than boys...this does not mean that females are better organized than males at all periods of life; in fact, females encounter more disorganizing illness than the males at middle age. Yet girls are better organized than boys in the formative period of life. They are more fluent in speech. (Bluemel)

The quotations and footnotes in this book have been taken from writings of speech pathologists and medical doctors, practically all of whom have been stutterers themselves. They understand your problem from observation and experience and represent a most distinguished array of authority and prestige in the field of stuttering. Their names are listed on page 185. Those who have been stutterers are marked with a star by the name.

On Self-Therapy

If you are like most of the million and a half stutterers in this country, adequate clinical treatment will not be available to you. Whatever you do you'll have to be pretty much on your own with what ideas and sources you can use.   (Sheehan)

The first thing you must do is to admit to yourself that you need to change, that you really want to do something about the way you presently talk. This is tough but your commitment must be total; not even a small part of you must hold back. Don't dwell longingly on your fluency in the magical belief that some day your speech blocks will disappear. There is no magic potion, no pink pill that will cure stuttering.

Don't sit around waiting for the right time for an inspiration to come to you—*you must go to it.* You must see that the old solutions, the things you have done to help yourself over the years simply do not work. Ruts wear deep though, and you will find it difficult to change. Even though the way you presently talk is not particularly pleasant, it is familiar. It is the unknown from which we shrink.

You must be willing to endure temporary discomfort, perhaps even agony, for the long range improvement you desire. No one is promising you a rose garden. Why not take the time and effort now for a lifetime of freedom from your tangled tongue? How can you do this? You break down the global problem of stuttering into its parts and then solve them one at a time. No one said it was easy. Shall we begin?   (Emerick)

A valuable precondition for a successful therapy is the deep inner conviction of the stutterer in the manage-ability of his disorder, combined with a fighting spirit and a readiness to undergo hardships and deprivations if needed—hopelessness, pessimism and passivity being the deadliest foes to self-improvement.   (Freund)

In case you are not familiar with the meanings of some of the words used in this book, you will find a glossary beginning on page 173 where definitions are given of terms and expressions used in the treatment of stuttering including many not found in this book. Read them for your general education in speech pathology.

On This Approach to Self-Therapy

This book is written to and for the many adult stutterers in this country[1]—and is addressed in the second person to describe what the stutterer can and should do to control his stuttering. We state confidently that as a stutterer you do not need to surrender helplessly to your speech difficulty because you can change the way you talk. You can learn to communicate with ease rather than with effort. There is no quick and easy way to tackle the problem but with the right approach self-therapy can be effective.

Experience has probably taught you to be skeptical about any plan which claims to offer a solution to your stuttering problem. You may have tried different treatment ideas and been disappointed and disillusioned in the past. This book promises no quick magical cure and makes no false claims.[2] It describes what you can and should do to overcome your difficulty.

It offers a logical practical program of therapy for the stutterer based on methods and procedures that have been used successfully in many universities and other speech clinics. This approach to therapy has been shown to get results. If there were an easier or better way of learning how to control stuttering we would recommend it.

---

[1]Almost one percent of the population of this country manifest some acute form of stammering speech, which places them under a great economic and social handicap. This can be corrected if given the proper training. (Martin) (Note: Stammering and stuttering are the same.)

[2]There are no quick or magical answers to your stuttering. (Barbara)

We start with two assumptions. One is that you have no physical defect or impairment of your speech mechanism. If you can talk without stuttering when you are alone or when not being heard or observed by others, it would be a fair assumption that you have no physical or organic defect causing your trouble.[1, 2, 3]Actually all stutterers have periods of fluency.

The other assumption is that you may not be in a position to avail yourself of the services of a speech pathologist, trained to help you work on your problem in the manner described in this book and that, as a result you need to be your own therapist. Even with competent guidance, authorities would agree that stuttering therapy is largely a do-it-yourself project anyway.[4, 5, 6, 7]

---

[1]There is no physical reason why you can't learn to speak more easily and fluently than you do now. (Johnson)

[2]There is nothing wrong inside your body that will stop you from talking. You have the same speaking equipment as anybody else. You have the ability to talk normally. (D. Williams)

[3]Because you stutter doesn't mean you are biologically inferior or more neurotic than the next person. (Sheehan)

[4]No one but myself improved my speech. Others have helped me by providing information, giving emotional support, identifying bias, etc. but the dirty work of therapy is, and always has been, my responsibility. (Boehmler)

[5]Don't ever forget that even if you went to the most knowledgeable expert in the country, the correction of stuttering is a do-it-yourself project. Stuttering is your problem. The expert can tell you what to do and how to do it, but you are the one who has to do it. You are the only person on earth who can correct your stuttering. (Starbuck)

[6]The stutterer must conquer his own problems—no one else can do the job for him. (VanRiper)

[7]Needless to say, each stutterer must from the beginning of therapy accept the responsibility for his problem. This implies self-therapy which is essential. (Stromsta)

If you are sincerely interested in working on your speech you will need to have a strong motivation to overcome your difficulty and a sincere determination to follow through on the suggested procedures and assignments. It will not be easy, but it can be done.

Obviously there is no way to promise success in this or any other program since no sure 'cure' for stuttering has yet been discovered, in spite of what you may have read. However, we believe that if you follow the suggestions and carry out the fluency procedures outlined in this book, you should be able to control your stuttering and speak easily without abnormality. Others have conquered their stuttering and you can too. But the best way for you to judge the effectiveness of any therapy program is to try it out and let the results speak for themselves.[1, 2]

It should be mentioned that there are many differences among stutterers. Some cases are mild and others severe and in most cases the frequency and severity of stuttering tends to vary from time to time and from one situation to another. Sometimes a stutterer may be able to speak comparatively fluently with little or no difficulty and at other times he may have considerable trouble. That tends to make it a most frustrating disorder since it can and usually does become worse in certain environments and under certain circumstances.

---

[1]A major problem in the treatment of stuttering is how to encourage the stutterer to stay in and continue with the course of treatment. (Barbara)

[2]Based on your understanding choose the most appropriate therapy program you can, and work at the program with more consistency, devotion and energy than any other task you've ever tackled. As success is obtained, maintain it with equal vigor. (Boehmler)

Usually a stutterer is more apt to have difficulty when embarrassed or when anticipating trouble. This may be more noticeable when asked to state his name or when talking to people in authority like prospective employers or teachers; in making introductions; when speaking to groups or talking on the telephone, etc. On the other hand the stutterer may have little or no trouble when talking to himself or talking to a child or pet animal.[1]

It should also be recognized that stutterers may vary widely in their reactions and characteristics and in the conditions under which their stuttering may occur. No two persons stutter in the same manner since every stutterer has developed his own particular pattern of stuttering.[2,3,4] Your reactions may be different from others and accordingly we ask you to bear with us when you read about troubles which you may not encounter yourself but which may represent a problem to others.

Most all stutterers have certain abilities which are somewhat surprising. Practically all stutterers generally have little or no difficulty when they sing or shout or whisper or read and speak in unison with others.

---

[1]Some stutterers have difficulty reading aloud; others do not. Some can speak well when in a position of authority; some show their greatest difficulty here. Some can use the telephone without interference; others are completely frustrated by this situation. Speaking with members of the opposite sex causes great difficulty to one stutterer but results in fluency with another. Some speak well at home but not in other environments; with others the situation is completely reversed. (Ansberry)

[2]The old saying that no two stutterers are alike is undoubtedly true. (Luper)

[3]The speech behavior patterns that have usually been associated with or identified as stuttering vary from person to person, and from time to time with any given person. (D. Williams)

[4]We all have different personalities and our pattern of stuttering is distinct and interwoven in the unique personalities. (Garland)

In your case if you have no difficulty when you read or speak in unison with others, that would indicate that you have the physiological ability to speak normally. It would also make it evident that psychological factors are the cause of a lot of your stuttering.

In this connection we would add that this in no way infers that any mental deficiency is involved since it has been shown that the IQ (intelligence quotient) of the average stutterer is normal or above normal.[1]

Equipment Desirable. For use in your work and study in this program it would help to have three items available. One is a reasonably large mirror (at least 15" x 18") which can be moved around unless it is now situated where you can observe yourself closely when talking on the telephone. And it would be most helpful if you could obtain the use of a small portable dictating machine or tape recorder[2, 3] of a size not much bigger than your hand which you can carry around with you to record your speech. It can be purchased at a fairly reasonable price. And you should also have on hand a small memorandum workbook.

Original Cause of Your Stuttering

One general comment is worth mentioning and should be of interest. There is no reason to be concerned about the original cause of your stuttering. Many

---

[1]On the whole people that stutter are highly intelligent and capable. (Barbara)

[2]A tape recorder will prove a good investment for the stammerer. (Bluemel)

[3]By using a tape recorder you tend to learn faster that your stuttering is, indeed, your own doing, and the changes you can make in what you do are very substantial. (Johnson)

theories have been advanced to explain its cause and nature, but none of them have been proven or seem provable. It may have been the result of environmental or hereditary factors or their interaction.

Whatever the cause, it is unlikely that it is still operating upon you or that it can be corrected at this late date. Therefore we do not believe that the original cause of your stuttering has or should have any bearing on or affect the therapy process.[1] You need to be concerned about what you are doing now that perpetuates and maintains your difficulty.

There is no reason for you to spend the rest of your life stuttering helplessly and making yourself miserable. Others have prevailed and so can you.

---

[1]Many stutterers have mistakenly believed that if only the "cause" could be found, a fast cure would result. (Murray)

Factors Affecting Therapy

Before explaining the specific steps to be used in therapy certain relevant factors should be discussed. This is because these factors have a bearing on and can affect your attitude toward or your ideas about treatment and how you can or should work on it.

These include information on subjects which can have a substantial influence on progress in therapy, such as a person's feelings, emotions, tensions, distractions, enlisting help from others, and motivations. We will start by pointing out how feelings and emotions can and frequently do affect the severity of your difficulty.

Your Feelings and Emotions

Stuttering is no simple speech impediment. It is a complicated disorder which has both physical and psychological aspects. To illustrate the latter, the statement can be made that stuttering is largely what the stutterer does trying not to stutter.[1] In other words it is an incredible trick which you play on yourself.

What happens is that you want to stop stuttering so badly that as a result you try to force trouble-free speech.[2] And the more you force the more tension is built up and the more trouble you are apt to have. Unfortunately, the mechanism of speech is so delicately balanced that in trying to stop stuttering, you unwittingly make it worse.

---

[1] In other words stuttering is what you do trying not to stutter again. (Johnson)

[2] The stutterer attempts to force the articulation of his words and speaking now becomes a muscular rather than a mental process. (Bluemel)

Stuttering affects one emotionally, since being a stutterer can be rough. Possibly you may think it's a disgrace to be a stutterer, even though that is not so, and as a result you may have become extremely sensitive about your difficulty.

It is true that the experience of being blocked or not being able to say what you want to say without stuttering can be really frustrating.[1] As a result, under some circumstances a stutterer may become so embarrassed and humiliated that he suffers from feelings of helplessness, shame, inferiority, depression and sometimes self-hatred.[2]

One's emotions may generate so much fear and anxiety that they can affect one's attitude toward others and life in general.[3, 4] Like the tail that wags the dog, stuttering can alter one's personality, but if you can become desensitized and learn that you do not have to panic when stuttering is anticipated or is experienced, progress will come more swiftly.

Stuttering fears can be of words or sounds, or of some persons, of certain situations, of the telephone, of saying your name, etc. When you have little fear you have less tension and probably don't have much difficulty.

---

[1]Fluency is a fair-weather friend that deserts the stutterer when he needs it most. (Sheehan)

[2]Talking was a highly emotional experience which gave me a feeling of helplessness, failure and defeat. (Freund)

[3]The stutterer develops emotional reactions which permeate his very soul, affect his will and upset his mind. (Martin)

[4]The stutterer feels at most times apart and different from others in his society. He feels that although others also have difficulties in life, they can cope with them and live much more easily with their problems. He feels more permanently crippled than others because of the fact that he cannot hide or conceal his speech difficulty, and therefore, he is the constant target of their embarrassment, ridicule and disapproval. (Barbara)

When your fear is strong it builds up tension and you will stutter more frequently and severely. Sometimes this fear can be so strong as to drive you frantic and almost paralyze thought and action.

Such fear or anxiety may prevent you from entering situations and experiences that you would otherwise enjoy. This can cause more shame and embarrassment, and the more frustrated you become, the more you are likely to stutter. So your stuttering is usually in proportion to the amount of fear you have.[1]

Tension and Relaxation

Since fear builds up excessive muscular tension its reduction should be a major goal of therapy. Tension, generated by fear, plays a most important part in activating your stuttering and may be the immediate triggering cause of your difficulty.[2,3] If you didn't try to force trouble-free speech you wouldn't stutter as much or at least you would stutter much more easily.

How can tension be reduced? That's difficult to answer. It has been suggested that hypnotism might help. It sure would be wonderful if you could reduce or elim-

---

[1]The more one stutters, the more he fears certain words and situations. The more he fears the more he stutters. The more he stutters the harder he struggles. The more he struggles, the more penalties he receives, and the greater becomes his fear. (Van Riper)

[2]Stuttering results when the speaker is unable to cope with excess muscular tension in the speech mechanism. (Luper)

[3]Stuttering then may be considered to be in large part something people do when they become unusually tense about the way they talk. (Bloodstein)

inate your tension by getting some sort of hypnotic treatment, but unfortunately it has not been shown that hypnosis has any permanent effect.[1]

Using another approach in an effort to effect relaxation, many stutterers have experimented with drinking alcoholic beverages or getting slightly intoxicated. We are sorry to report that although this is usually conducive to lessening tension and in most cases to less stuttering, its effect can only be temporary. So obviously it can not be recommended.[2, 3]

Nor, unfortunately, are there any drugs which can be recommended.[4, 5]Tranquilizers do not do the job.[6, 7]

---

[1]Many of you have heard about the wonders of hypnosis and may look to this technique to provide a quick answer. Rest assured that this has been tried throughout the years, but almost invariably with only temporary and fleeting success. (Murray)

[2]I turned to smoking excessively and drinking occasionally but found no solace there. (Wedberg)

[3]One of my patients was a city official who made a practice of taking whisky before giving his weekly report to the City Council. Soon his alcoholism became a more serious problem than his stammering, and he was hospitalized for this condition. (Bluemel)

[4]Drug treatment is strictly contraindicated. (Brown)

[5]How wonderful it would be if we could toss a pill down the throat of a stutterer and hear no more stuttering. Unfortunately we have no such panacea. (Adler)

[6]There are modern sedatives which diminish tension without inducing sleep. They may be used in an emergency but should not be relied upon to relieve a continued condition such as stammering. (Bluemel)

[7]Since the exacerbation of stuttering by anxiety is a common experience, it might be assumed that drugs that relieve anxiety would be beneficial. However, minor tranquilizers have been tried many times without success. (Rosenberger)

It has also been suggested that relaxation exercises would help to reduce or eliminate the tension that a stutterer experiences. It sure would be great if one could practice relaxation procedures which would eliminate that tension and retain their effectiveness. A lot of research has gone into studying this subject and many stutterers have spent thousands of hours trying out such procedures and hoping that their effect would carry over to their time of need, but the results have not proved very satisfactory.[1]

This does not mean that relaxation measures are discouraged as learning to relax can always benefit one's general health and well-being even if they are not indicated as a solution to the problem. Still the fundamental principle would still hold that the more calm and relaxed you are, the less stuttering you will do. That's one reason you will be asked to talk in a smooth, slow, easy and deliberate manner since it will help to induce a calmer and more relaxed way of communication.

More practical than general relaxation is the relaxation of specific muscles. When you can locate the place where the most tension is, it is possible that you could learn to relax those muscles during speech.[2] There are certain differential muscle relaxation exercises that are helpful under special circumstances.

---

[1] Relaxation has sometimes been described as a method in and of itself for the treatment of stuttering. I do not believe, however, that relaxation procedures have much permanent value unless they are part of a more inclusive therapeutic process. (Gregory)

[2] Once the stutterer has localized the places in the vocal tract where he habitually exerts too much tension, he may practice stuttering with less of it. (Bloodstein)

These exercises involve only certain muscles, the ones you use to control your lips, your tongue, your mouth, your breath and to some extent your vocal chords. When you are relaxed and alone you could practice purposely tensing and then relaxing those muscles. It would certainly be beneficial if you could relax these muscles during speech.

The regular practice of calisthenics or body exercises of that type is also recommended. The thought is that physical exercises are not only good for one's health but can contribute to building the self-confidence which most stutterers need.

And that would be true since body exercises can help build an inclination to stand up straight with head erect and shoulders back.[1] That kind of assertive posture can help generate a feeling of self-confidence—the feeling that you are as good (or better) than the next person.[2] In that respect physical exercises will help you.

---

[1] Accept the fact that you have a serious problem. Stand squarely on both feet, place your shoulders back and begin to earnestly attack your problem. (Barbara)

[2] Assume an assertive posture—physically be committed to moving forward. Use your body language to advantage (G. F. Johnson)

Distractions

If there were some way you could distract your mind from thoughts of fear, so that you didn't think about your stuttering, probably you would have practically no trouble.[1] If you could forget you were a stutterer you might not stutter at all, but we don't know how you could develop such a "forgettery."

Anything that distracts your mind from fear or takes your mind off the threat of stuttering usually will give you temporary relief. This is the main reason why stutterers are sometimes misled by tricky procedures such as talking with sing-song inflection, or with metronone timing, or talking while tapping a finger, swinging an arm, or stamping a foot, etc. These and many other odd ways of talking may produce temporary fluency.

Just thinking about how to use them when you anticipate trouble, shifts your attention and may temporarily blot out thoughts of fear but does not result in any permanent reduction of fear or stuttering. Strange as it may seem almost any new or bizarre technique[2,3] may help a stutterer—at least until the novelty wears off—if he develops confidence in its effectiveness and is susceptible to suggestion.

---

[1]If he forgot he was a stutterer and simply went ahead on the assumption that he would have no difficulty, he would speak quite normally. (Bloodstein)

[2]One of the tricky features of undertaking therapy with stutterers is that anything in the way of technique to bring about immediate fluency is likely to work at least temporarily. (Sheehan)

[3]Witchcraft, the surgeon's knife, appliances for the tongue, drugs, hypnotism, psychoanalysis, arm swinging and a host of other devices and methods have been employed and a few 'cures' seem to be obtained by any method, no matter how grotesque. (VanRiper)

Enlisting the Support of Others

It would be fortunate if you could get the help of a competent speech pathologist who has been trained in the field of stuttering. However, this self-therapy program has been planned under the assumption that you may not have such specialized help. Even if you did, the success of any program would largely be dependent on yourself.[1, 2]

That does not mean that you should discourage help from others since you need people to talk with and practice on. If you have a member of your family or a close friend with whom you have a good and trusting relationship and in whom you have confidence, he or she may be able to render you valuable service in many ways.[3]

Acting as an observer, such a person may be able to see and hear things of which you may not be aware. It is also possible when you are studying the way you stutter (which will be discussed later), such a friend could try to duplicate your stuttering to help you become aware of what you are doing when you are having trouble.[4]

Or he or she could accompany you on some of your

---

[1]The stutterer must get out of his mind that he can be "cured" by somebody else. (Wedberg)

[2]Before you begin to follow any specific program for correcting your stutter you must remember that stuttering is your problem and yours alone. (Barbara)

[3]What I needed was not an authority but a friend and collaborator genuinely interested in me and ready to help me. I was fortunate to have a brother who could be this friend. (Freund)

[4]My high school chemistry teacher, a former stutterer, gave up his lunch hour twice a week to talk with me about speech...Perhaps you can find this kind of sympathetic friend who will listen while you talk about your stuttering. Let him know that you do not expect advice. You don't expect him to be clinician, just a friend. (Brown)

assignments, compliment you on your efforts, give you moral support by encouraging you to carry on and persevere until you reach your goal. You need all the encouragement you can get.

(Sometimes friends with the best of intentions offer unsolicited advice about what they have heard or think you should do to overcome your stuttering. Although such advice may be unwise and unwanted, it is suggested that it should be accepted gracefully even though it is based on an inadequate understanding of what is causing the difficulty.)

Your Determination

There is no easy road to fluency. For therapy to accomplish its purpose it will take determination.[1] It is necessary for you to have the courage to confront[2] your stuttering head-on and undertake assignments which will require a lot of work and probably embarrassment. Is more fluent speech worth the effort which you must go through to produce it? That is up to you.

Actually, the embarrassment you may experience will help reduce the sensitivity which makes your stuttering worse.[3] And becoming less sensitive to your difficulty will make it easier for you to retain sufficient presence of mind to carry through on the recommended procedures.

If you feel your stuttering is a handicap, you need to find ways and means for having a richer life through

---

[1]You appreciate most in life those things you do for yourself. Getting over stuttering takes tremendous self-discipline and desire. (Aten)

[2]Although it is a tough row to hoe at first, there is nothing as therapeutic as self-confrontation. (Rainey)

[3]At some point in the therapy process the stutterer must become desensitized to his stuttering. (Kamhi)

more fluent speech. [1] You need to feel better about yourself as a person. Although you should not demand or expect perfection, you want to speak more freely. But to do this you need the determination to make changes in your way of talking and in yourself that can put you in control and make you master of your speech.

We say that you can and that the pay-off is far greater than the cost. But it will take dedication on your part to change your attitude toward your problem. [2] Stuttering is a stubborn handicap and it will not give up easily. [3, 4] Therapy is a challenge. [5] The decision is yours.

---

[1] I still remember vividly what a severe stutterer and how tangled emotionally I once was. When I see any stutterer I remember my own unfavorable prognosis, my own weakness, my lack of hope, and when I do, I find in the case before me strengths and potentials which I did not have. If I could do what I have done, then surely this person could do as much. This is a very real faith, and I suspect it has played a large part in any success I have had as a clinician. (VanRiper)

[2] Leonard, a stutterer, would try anything although never in a reckless or foolhardy fashion. He possessed both discernment enough to see what needed to be done and guts enough to do it—a happy combination for a stutterer. He had kind of a stubbornness or dogged persistence that he was able to turn into an asset. (Sheehan)

[3] Stuttering is a tough opponent. It never gives up. You've got to keep knocking it down to stay in command. (Starbuck)

[4] A valuable precondition for successful therapy is the deep inner conviction of the stutterer in the creditability of his disorder—combined with a fighting spirit and a readiness to undergo hardships and deprivations. (Freund)

[5] Men who have achieved in this world have been guided by inspiration, by vision, by faith in themselves and by faith in the unknown. (Wedberg)

The Premise and the Program

The ideas expressed in this book are based on the premise that stuttering is not a symptom of something but is a behavior that can be modified.[1] This means that you can learn to control your difficulty, partly through modifying your feelings and attitudes about stuttering, and partly through modifying the irregular behaviors associated with your stuttering blocks.[2, 3, 4]

This will involve reducing your fear of having difficulty by disciplining yourself to face your fears and become less sensitive about your stuttering.[5, 6]And it will include analyzing your stuttering behavior, eliminat-

---

[1]The basic fact revealed by these laboratory and clinical studies was that the behavior called stuttering is extremely modifiable. It is possible for a speaker to change drastically the things he does that he calls his stuttering. (Johnson)

[2]Your fundamental task is twofold: alter your speech behavior, and bring about positive changes in your self-perception and feelings. (Murray)

[3]During the process of therapy he (the stutterer) should learn by experience that he can change his speaking behavior and that he can change his emotional reactions, both to the way he talks and toward his listeners and himself. (D. Williams)

[4]Basically there are two principal features of his behavior that the stutterer can alter. One is the speech behavior itself and the other is his attitude toward speaking and stuttering in particular. These two aspects are related: one of the ways change of attitude is brought about is by helping the stutterer to experience an ability to modify his speech, and one way in which speech is changed is through the reduction of fear which accompanies a different way of thinking about the problem. (Gregory)

[5]Somehow you must learn to desensitize yourself to the reactions of others and refuse to let people's actual or imagined responses to your stuttering continue to affect your mental health or peace of mind. (Adler)

[6]One of the most important phases of the treatment of the adult stutterer is that which attempts to change the shame and embarrassment that are associated with the act of stuttering. (VanRiper)

ing what you do which is unnecessary or abnormal, and taking positive action to control your blocks. The basic principle is that stuttering is something you are doing and you can learn to change what you are doing.[1]

About the Program

Since it is important for you to understand the overall therapy plan, we explain briefly how this program works. First you will be asked to try out an experimental therapy procedure described in the chapter entitled An Experimental Therapy Procedure. This will be particularly beneficial for those who feel they need some immediate relief.

Then it is suggested that you comply with twelve common sense helpful recommendations or ground rules to improve your speech. These ground rules are designed to supply you with practical ways of coping with your difficulty.

By complying with the recommendations of these rewarding ground rules you will be concentrating on both reducing the severity and abnormality of your difficulty and reducing the number of your stutterings. And when you carry out the provisions of these guidelines, you will be gradually laying the groundwork for gaining positive control of your speech.

These rules or guidelines will urge you among other things to talk more deliberately, stutter more easily and

---

[1]Your stuttering is something you do, not something that happens to you. It is your behavior—not a condition. There are mistakes you can correct with a little self-study and courage. (Sheehan)

openly, make no effort to hide your stuttering, stop all avoidance practices, eliminate your secondary symptoms, maintain normal eye contact, etc.

One particularly important rule will call for you to make a detailed study of what you are doing incorrectly with your speech mechanism when you stutter. In other words find out specifically what you are doing when you run into trouble.[1,2] This essential information will be used to help you change or eliminate those things you are doing abnormally which make your speech a problem and help you learn better ways of coping with your stuttering when it is anticipated or occurs.[3]

Then you will be instructed how to cope with these irregularities by using post-block, in-block and pre-block corrections to modify or eliminate your faulty speech mechanism behavior. These corrections are designed to help you move more smoothly through feared words in a predetermined manner to enable you to develop a feeling of control.

When you find that you can comply with the ground rules you will have made progress in controlling your speech. Some rule or rules may affect your stuttering and mean more to you than some of the others, because they may hit your weak points. As a result you may find that attaining the goal of some rule or rules may contribute more to progress in your case.

---

[1]The first phase of therapy involves assisting persons who stutter to attend to what they are doing as they stutter. (D. Williams)

[2]You've got to examine and analyze the act of speaking to see what errors you're making. You must be making mistakes somewhere or you would be speaking fluently. What are you doing that makes your speech come out as stuttering? (Starbuck)

[3]For some stutterers simply identifying stutterings as they are being produced is sufficient to enable them to start modifying these very same instances of stuttering. (Conture)

Unfortunately there is no way for us to know the particular way you stutter so we can only suggest that you try to follow through on all the recommendations.

The length of time needed to accomplish the objective of each rule will vary considerably according to the severity of your case, and your resolution in working on the assignments. It is possible that the time required to reach some desired goal can be measured in days, but for some stutterers it may take a long time to bring under control some stubborn or seemingly uncontrollable practice or habit.[1, 2]

Even if your stuttering is mild you are urged to move through each phase of the program.[3] And when you tackle a guideline we hope you will feel satisfied that you have reasonably achieved its goal or purpose before proceeding to the next one. By doing this you will know exactly where you stand and what progress you are making.

Learning how to help yourself should be the goal of every stutterer. Your first step will be for you to experiment with a different way of talking as described in the next chapter. This is designed to give you some immediate relief.

---

[1]The adult stutterer enters therapy...the first thing he must understand is that stuttering as it now exists was acquired over a period of time, and that change is a process which will be gradual—not sudden. (Gregory)

[2]But you say you want to stop stuttering. Sure! But first you need to break up the habit pattern that you have built up over the years and this cannot be done instantly. (Emerick)

[3]Therefore we must proceed up a long ladder of sub-goals, each of which takes you closer to the conquest of your speech defect. (VanRiper)

An Experimental
Therapy Procedure

This procedure is particularly for those stutterers who feel that they need some immediate relief even if it is temporary. However, it is suggested that every stutterer should try out this experimental procedure, since it can help one to talk more fluently. It involves using an easy onset and a very slow smooth easy prolonged manner of talking.

This may not be the answer to your problem but this procedure is being used in certain college and university speech clinics. It somewhat resembles the manner of speaking effected through the use of 'delayed auditory feedback' equipment (See definition in glossary) which has been shown to promote fluency with stutterers.

And it is claimed that it cannot help but give a stutterer some immediate relief, and furthermore with diligent practice has alleviated the problem for some stutterers. Although it is possible for you to skip this particular procedure, we recommend that you try out this manner of talking.

(See next page for details on how to follow through on this method of treatment.)

Specifics

As you are aware, words are made up of sounds. In this procedure you are asked to start the sounds of your words at an extremely slow easy smooth rate. In other words start saying your words by relaxedly sliding extremely slowly through the beginning sounds. This could mean taking as long as a second or more to slide through the sounds that start your words.[1]

Then stretch out and prolong all sounds as you voice them using continuous phonation. That means stretching out and prolonging every consonant and vowel sound, and sliding through and slowing the transition from one sound to the next sound.[2]

To do this start your vocal cords vibrating in a low steady very slow way as you begin to articulate words in this easy onset manner with light easy contacts. This slow drawn-out manner of talking will result in your having continuity of sound and air flow with no break in your voice and no repetitions. To repeat, stretch out and prolong all your voicing of sounds. And prolong all transitions between all sounds (consonant and vowel) with light easy contacts on the consonants.

It is easy to stretch out and prolong vowel sounds, but you will need to practice stretching many of the consonant sounds.[3] Spend time when alone practicing how to increase the duration of consonant sounds as some of

---

[1] Audible sound prolongations are excellent places to start modifications with adult stutterers. (Conture)

[2] What is required to facilitate fluency is to slow the speed of transitional movements from sound to sound which is what prolongation of voice sounds provides. (Perkins)

[3] Achieve the proper slow rate not by pausing between words, but by stretching each vowel and consonant. Vowels are easy to stretch. Consonants are hard. (Guitar-Peters)

them like t, d, p, b, etc. are plosive but can be spoken easily and slowly with light or loose contacts of the tongue and mouth.

This smooth, slow, easy, drawn out manner of talking should be used on non-feared words as well as feared words. In short it should be done all the time you talk until you get the knack of it. Bind the sounds of your words together, hitch the beginning of one word to the tail of the one preceding it.

It will embarrass you some to talk at this easy smooth slow rate of only some 30 words per minute but you need to find out what it can do for you. Start using this procedure while carrying on conversation with others only after you have spent considerable time practicing this method of talking when you are alone.

Talking in this smooth easy onset manner should enable a severe stutterer, or most any stutterer for that matter to communicate without difficulty. To repeat it is recommended that you use this prolonged way of talking when speaking to others only after you have spent considerable time practicing it when alone.

You may hesitate to talk this way because you feel that people will wonder why you are doing so. Tell them the truth that you are working on your stuttering. There is nothing to be ashamed of, and people who are close to you will be glad to help. After using this manner of talking for some time then one may very slowly and gradually increase the rate at which words are spoken unless trouble occurs in which case the slower rate should be used at which no difficulty was incurred.

Even though you feel that this easy onset slow flowing manner of talking may not solve your problem, give it an opportunity to see what it can do for you. It is a commonly used procedure which can give you considerable relief and enable you to speak more easily.

In any event it will show yourself and others that you are accepting your stuttering as a problem, not as a curse, and trying to cope with it. People respect that attitude. Start now.

Conscientiously work for some time—at least a week or more on the program as described above. By then you will know what benefit you can derive from this approach to therapy.

Reminder—the footnotes in this book have been taken from the writings of men and women who have been speech pathologists and have distinguished themselves in the field of stuttering. Most of them earned degrees as doctors of philosophy or medicine and have known what you are up against as they have been stutterers themselves. Their names and titles are listed starting on page 185.

The All-Important Ground Rules

Adopting Rewarding Habits and Beneficial Practices

We hope that experimenting with the procedure advocated in the last chapter enabled you to communicate more easily with less difficulty. However, of course, we cannot and would not recommend that you permanently employ this manner of talking.

The rules described below in this chapter will explain how to manage your stuttering by putting into effect certain basic remedial practices. These consist of twelve all-important rules or guidelines which briefly summarize this program. In a general way they outline how you can manage your difficulty by taking advantage of two approaches.

First, through modifying your feelings and attitudes about your stuttering by decreasing your speech fears and avoidance behaviors. Second, through modifying the irregular behaviors associated with your stuttering by using certain techniques which can change the form of your stuttering so you can speak without abnormality.

There are twelve of these rules. We wish we could recommend a more simple program, but unfortunately, as has been pointed out, stuttering is a complicated disorder. Therefore, it is advisable to take advantage of the various approaches available which can work toward solving your problem.

It is suggested that you read over and carefully study the following rules and guidelines as described on the next few pages. To make progress it is necessary for you to do your best to comply with each of these beneficial practices as described—working on them one at a time.

It would seem desirable to tackle them in the order in which they are listed, although that is a matter of discretion. As listed, the rules are directed generally at first reducing what sensitivity you may have about your stuttering and stopping all avoidance habits, etc. Then you will concentrate on correcting what you are doing wrong when you stutter.

Toward this latter objective an important rule will call for you to make a detailed study of what you are doing unnaturally with your speech mechanism as you stutter. Then this information will be employed to enable you to eliminate those things you are doing unnecessarily and correct what you are doing wrong.

To rectify your faulty speech mechanism behavior you will be instructed to use post-block, in-block and pre-block corrections. These corrections are designed to help you move smoothly through feared words in a predetermined manner so you can develop a feeling of control.

Working on accomplishing the objectives of these rules will not be easy—in fact, it can be a long drawn-out, worrisome process. Obviously, it will take time and determination not only to work on reducing your fear of difficulty but also to modify the pattern of your speaking behavior.

Some rule or rules may affect your stuttering and mean more to you than others because they may hit your weak points. As a result you may find that attaining the goal of some rule or rules may contribute to more progress in your case. Unfortunately, there is no way for us to know your particular weaknesses so we can only suggest that you follow through on all the recommendations.

Remember, you are your own therapist and you may have no one to supervise you if you do not follow through on these rules. Perfect compliance is not possible and is not expected but results are what you want and need.

Working on these beneficial practices should be the key to your making progress in achieving what you want done. Make a real effort to sincerely comply with each of these guidelines to the best of your ability. It will be worthwhile.

Give yourself a strong dose of willpower and have confidence in your ability to make progress. The next chapters following this rules chapter will explain explicitly how to work on achieving the objective of each rule. Here they are—let's go to work on them.

(There are a few stutterers who feel little or no shame or embarrassment about their stuttering. As a result those in that classification who would have little or no fear of difficulty, would not be as concerned about the rules or guidelines which are directed at reducing the shame and embarrassment which most stutterers have.)

Therapy must be practiced full time to be highly suc-cessful. You must feel that you are on the right track and you must be committed to putting the program into practice. Plan your work well, then work your plan harder than you have ever worked before. Success will follow. (Boehmler)

(1)Make a habit of always talking slowly and deliberately whether you stutter or not. It is always better to go too slow than too fast.[1] It is easier to control a slow turtle than a fast rabbit, so slow down.

This first rule or guideline calls for you to build the habit of always talking slowly and deliberately. This induces a manner of talking which is generally respected, but is mainly recommended because it will result in a more varied and relaxed manner of speaking which is more responsive to therapy controlled procedures.[2]

Also, talking deliberately tends to counteract feelings of time pressure that stutterers sometimes get when called on to speak. Occasionally, they think they have no time to lose and so must hurry to get their words out which just generates tension and aggravates their stuttering.[3] To help reduce such feelings it is also suggested that when the stutterer talks, he might pause or even stop momentarily between phrases (or sentences) to help lessen time pressure reactions.

Temporarily accepting your role as a stutterer, let's resolve to make a special effort to talk slowly and deliberately all the time. This will not be easy to do and will take concentration, particularly if you have been in the habit of speaking rapidly. This may feel unnatural at first but if you can adjust to that manner of talking, it will be beneficial and you will be under much less time pressure.

(See instructions—page 61)

---

[1]Talk slowly and deliberately. (Agnello)

[2]Rate is a particularly useful clinical entry point for establishing fluency and maintaining it. (Perkins)

[3]Panic, tension and an overwhelming urgency are the hallmark of stuttering: they are what you need to overcome. (J. D. Williams)

(2) When you stutter, stutter easily, gently and smoothly without forcing. That means talking firmly with your voice smoothly flowing into the sounds of words with light loose movements of your lips, tongue and jaw[1]. Gently, easily and smoothly sliding into words is sometimes referred to as easy onset.

This most important guideline suggests that when you stutter do it in as easy and calm manner as possible, with normal quiet breathing.[2] If you can comply with this one rule and let yourself stutter easily, your severity will lessen and so will the frequency of your stuttering.

Stutterers try to cope with their problem by trying to force words out at the same time as they close off the airway by squeezing the lips together, or pressing the tongue tightly against the roof of the mouth, or clamping shut their vocal cords. This makes no sense. You can't pour water out of a corked bottle. Explore how easily you can stutter.

There is nothing to be gained by forcing or struggling.[3] The more you try to force trouble-free speech, the worse your stuttering will be. Quit fighting yourself— you are bound to lose. Substitute easier ways of stuttering for your abnormal and frustrating habits.[4] Stutter easily and calmly. You will feel the difference.

(See instructions—page 65)

---

[1]Many stutterers have learned as I have learned that it is possible to stutter easily with little struggle and tension. (Sheehan)

[2]Try to stutter more openly, more easily. (Emerick)

[3]Your immediate goal should be to allow yourself to stutter openly and without tension and struggle. (Murray)

[4]You must learn to substitute easy, slower, more relaxed movements for rushed, tight, forced movements. (Aten)

(3) Stutter openly and do not try to hide the fact that you are a stutterer. There is no advantage in pretending that you are a normal speaker. [1,2] Trying to hide your stuttering only helps to perpetuate it. Tell others that you stutter and adopt an attitude of being willing to stutter voluntarily.

If you adopt a frank and open attitude, it will help to reduce what shame or embarrassment you may have about your difficulty. Feelings of shame or embarrassment tend to increase your fear of difficulty. And this fear of difficulty helps to build up tension or tightness in your speaking apparatus which aggravates your trouble. [3]

If stutterers did not try to hide the fact that they stutter, most of them would be less sensitive about their problem and as a result have much less difficulty. To change your mental approach and reduce your self-consciousness may be a difficult assignment as it will take time to get rid of your fear. However, the more you work at it, the happier you will be.

Therefore, let's work on reducing what fear you may have about your speech by willingly admitting to others that you are a stutterer. Make occasion to discuss it with those with whom you talk. [4,5] Tell them you are working on your speech.

---

[1] The first thing you must become is an honest stutterer. (Starbuck)

[2] Many stutterers will go to any lengths to conceal from others the fact that they stutter. There is great fear of losing face. (Murray)

[3] If you are like all of the other adult stutterers I have known, you create, without meaning to, of course, a major share of any adjustment difficulties you may have...by trying to cover up, conceal or disguise the fact that you talk the way you do. (Johnson)

[4] They should cultivate the ability to discuss their stuttering casually and objectively with others.(Bloodstein)

[5] You need to communicate more openly and easily with other people including being frank about your stuttering. (Boland)

As part of this guideline you will be encouraged to sometimes stutter voluntarily on purpose. By deliberately doing what you dread you may be able to get some relief from the fear and tension which aggravates your problem. However, before doing so, please read the recommendations in the chapter on admitting that you stutter.

(See instructions—page 69)

Yes, I am a stutterer, and I hope that it will help any stutterer who may read this to know that I was such a severe stutterer that I could not put two meaningful words together until I was twenty-four years old. Do I still stutter? Oh, I call myself a stutterer because I still have small interruptions in my speech now and then. But, there's another more important reason why I call myself a stutterer. I'm not trying to hide the fact anymore! (Rainey)

(4) Do your best to stop all avoidance, post-ponement or substitution habits which you may have acquired to put off, hide or minimize your stuttering. It is very important to make a practice of not avoiding, postponing or substituting.[1]

Much of a stutterer's difficulty may be traced to avoidance practices. While temporarily affording relief, such habits actually increase one's fears and cause more trouble in the long run.[2] For instance, if the telephone rings and you refuse to answer, because you are afraid you won't be able to talk well, the act of avoiding this situation will only tend to build up your fear of the telephone.[3]

Therefore, a stutterer should do his best to not dodge speaking situations, avoid social contacts, give up speech attempts or leave the scene of approaching trouble, substitute words or use postponements.[4]

This can be a really tough assignment but many authorities feel that a non-avoidance attitude will give the stutterer more relief than any other therapy procedure.[5] Avoidances have been described as a pump in the reservoir of fear.

---

[1]Don't avoid certain words or situations that trigger stuttering. Face them head-on. It's far better to stutter than to avoid speaking situations because the fear of stuttering just compounds the problem. (Murray)

[2]And what actually happens is that the more you cover up and try to avoid stuttering the more you will stutter, (Barbara)

[3]Avoidance can be defined as a process of shying away from the responsibility of facing your problems. (La Porte)

[4]You must sharply reduce or eliminate the avoidances you use. Everytime you substitute one word for another, use a sound or some trick to get speech started, postpone or give up an attempt at talking, you make it harder for yourself. (Emerick)

[5]The more you run away from your stuttering, the more you will stutter. The more you are open and courageous, the more you will develop solid fluency. (Sheehan)

It would be great if you could develop a feeling inside yourself that you will eagerly hunt out and eliminate avoidances.[1,2] This feeling will come if you can make a practice of doing things you fear without giving yourself time to talk yourself out of them. It is very important for the stutterer to establish speech that is avoidance-free.

(See instructions—page 77)

---

[1] The stutterer should develop a conscience which itself will penalize the tendancy to avoid. (VanRiper)

[2] One of the primary concerns of therapy is to develop in stutterers a conscience that prevents them from avoiding stuttering. (Bloodstein)

<u>**(5) Identify and eliminate any abnormal body movements or habits**</u> which you may exhibit when trying to avoid difficulty. This refers to unnecessary mannerisms or noticeable movements characterizing the particular pattern of the way you stutter.

Later you will investigate your abnormal speech muscle movements but this rule refers to movements which are called secondary symptoms. These include antics such as head jerks, hand or arm movements, mouth or facial contorsions, eye blinks or closings, finger snapping, finger or foot tappings, knees slapping, raising eyebrows, covering your mouth with your hand, etc.[1]

Possibly you exhibit no unnatural behaviors, but check yourself carefully as described in the chapter on eliminating secondary symptoms. If you find that you have such behaviors, let's work on getting rid of them. Obviously, they are not necessary for the production of speech.[2]

To accomplish this it will be necessary to find out and identify what your secondary symptoms may be.[3] This information is needed so you can work at eliminating them. These would be bad habits which you may have fallen into, thinking they would help you speak more easily but only add to the abnormality of your stuttering.

(See instructions—page 87)

---

[1]Become aware of head or arm movements, eye blinking, other movements or body rigidity, lip smacking or other noises, puffing of the cheeks or pressing the lips. (Moses)

[2]He (the stutterer) will learn, much to his surprise that these secondary symptoms are not an integral part of his disorder, that it is possible for him to stutter without using them. (VanRiper)

[3]When these reactions are recognized as secondary symptoms, they can gradually be minimized and controlled and the stammerer is then in a better position to contend with the primary speech disorder. (Bluemel)

(6) Maintain eye contact with the person to whom you talk. Possibly you may already do so, but if not, start looking your listener in the eye more or less continuously in a natural way.[1] It is particularly important for you not to look away when you stutter or expect to.

Possibly because they are ashamed of their speech difficulty, many stutterers have a tendency to avoid looking at their listener when stuttering.[2] Using continuous normal eye contact will work toward reducing feelings of shame and embarrassment. If you do not already maintain healthy normal eye contact, concentrate on doing so.[3]

(See instructions—page 95)

---

[1]Establish eye contact before you begin to speak. Two or three seconds of quiet eye contact can get you off to a better start. (Sheehan)

[2]Try to maintain eye contact with your listeners. Looking away severs the communication link with your audience and convinces them that you are ashamed and disgusted with the way you talk. (Moses)

[3]Maintaining eye contact may sound easy. For many people it is very hard. I know stutterers who have gone through various therapies with some success but who still have been unable to break their old habit of looking away from their listener when a block begins. (Murray)

(7) Explore and analyze what your speech muscles are doing improperly when you stutter. It is an essential and very important part of this program for you to be able to identify specifically the various kinds of things you are having your speech muscles do when you have trouble.[1]

This is so you can find out what you are doing wrong or unnecessarily which needs to be modified or corrected.[2] In other words since you are using your speech muscles unnaturally when you stutter, it is important for you to discover what you are having them do incorrectly so you can work on correcting what is being done improperly.[3,4]

Taking advantage of and making use of such an investigation is a key point in therapy. We urge you to follow through on this rule and study your speech muscle behavior so you can duplicate it in order to compare it with your speech when you talk without difficulty.[5, 6]

---

[1]When a problem exists, the first thing to do is to examine it carefully with the hope of discovering what is wrong. (Rainey)

[2]Try to identify what you are doing wrong when you stutter. (Emerick).

[3]Another important goal in your search for an ultimate cure is to acquaint yourself with your stuttering behavior. (Barbara)

[4]Pay enough attention to the things you do that interfere with your normal speech, the things you do that you call your stuttering; that is, to understand that they are unnecessary and to change or eliminate them. (Johnson)

[5]For some stutterers simply identifying stutterings as they are being produced is sufficient to enable them to start modifying these very same instances of stuttering. (Conture)

[6]Stutterers need to learn what to do when they do stutter if they are to eventually reduce the fear and frustration involved. (Czuchna)

There are various ways of observing one's self. One way would be to hold on to your stuttering blocks long enough to determine what you are doing or stutter slowly enough to give you time to get the feel of what is happening. Or watch yourself in the mirror when making phone calls—or listen to a playback of a tape recording of your speech, etc.

It will take courage to do these things but you definitely want this information to help solve your problem so you will become fully aware of what needs to be modified or corrected.[1, 2] With this information it should be possible for you to answer the questions—what am I doing—why am I doing it—and what else can I do.

(See the chapter on finding out what you do when you stutter—and on analyzing blocks. That chapter, page 99, has a section explaining how one stutterer could work on saying his name without difficulty.)

---

[1] The stutterer must come to know just what he does when he approaches a feared word or situation. (VanRiper)

[2] You, as a stutterer, must study your speech pattern in order to become aware of the differences between stuttered and fluent speech. (Neely)

(8) Take advantage of block correction procedures designed to modify or eliminate your abnormal speech muscle stuttering behavior.

These procedures are called post-block, in-block and pre-block corrections and are described in detail in the chapters on block corrections. They are employed to help you develop a feeling of control by taking advantage of the knowledge gained from the study of your blocking difficulties as discussed under Rule (7).

These are to be put to work only after you have studied and identified what you are doing abnormally with your speech mechanism when you stutter. With the use of this information the block corrections referred to above will help you eliminate, modify or correct these abnormalities.[1, 2, 3]

(See chapters on block corrections.)

---

[1]Stuttering consists mainly of learned behavior. This behavior can be unlearned. (Murray)

[2]Stuttered forms of speech can be changed in various ways just as handwriting can be modified. It is this changing of an established habit that requires work. (Neely)

[3]After the stutterer gains the knowledge of how he stutters through block analysis, he is ready to attack and defeat his most dreaded enemy. This is accomplished by the use of post-block, in-block and pre-block corrections. (Starbuck)

(9) Always keep moving forward as you speak, unless you repeat purposely to emphasize a word or thought. If you stutter, stutter forward so as not to hold or repeat any sound. Speech is an ongoing process, moving forward from one sound to the next.

When you start and voice a sound, there is no use of holding or making it over again.[1] Continuing the flow of your voice will work against any tendency to hold a block, prolong or repeat sounds on which trouble is anticipated.[2]

The idea is to speak words moving or sliding slowly and firmly from one word to the next until they are uttered. When you anticipate trouble on a word, plan to say the whole word rather than the first sound. Keep the vowel strongly in mind and possibly prolong the transition between all sounds but keep the voice moving forward.[3]

In other words try to say what you have to say without repeating or back-tracking at all. Going back to get a running start may possibly get you past a block but will never get you anywhere worthwhile. So do your best not to repeat or hold sounds, words or anything unless you are repeating purposely to emphasize a word or thought.

---

[1]Why continue to make a sound when you have already produced it? (VanRiper)

[2]The stutterer needs to stutter forward. He needs to go ahead...without regard to anticipated difficulty. (Sheehan)

[3]Keep going forward slowly but positively. (J. D. Williams)

(10) Try to talk with inflection and melody in a firm voice without sounding affected or artificial. Avoid talking in a monotone and keep varying your speaking rate and its loudness. Speak in a melodious manner without sounding artificial. Using natural expression with variations in tone and rate will make your talking more relaxing and pleasant.

(11) Pay attention to the fluent speech you have. Don't just be aware of your stuttering. Listen to yourself when you are fluent.[1] You need to recognize and remember your successful and pleasant speaking experiences. Mentally replay successful speaking situations and feel your fluency to build your confidence.

Remind yourself that you have the ability to speak fluently. To help give yourself that feeling, spend time speaking or reading to yourself when relaxed and alone. Do some of this while watching yourself in the mirror. As you do it be conscious of the fact that it is possible for you to speak easily without effort in a normal way without difficulty.

---

[1]Pay more attention to your normal speech than to what you think of as you're stuttering. (Johnson)

(12) While working on this program **try to talk as much as you can** since you will need every opportunity to work on the procedures recommended. This does not mean that you should make a nuisance of yourself but talk more—you've probably been silent long enough. Speak out when you want to.[1, 2, 3] If opportunities to talk do not exist, you should do your best to create opportunities. Let others hear your ideas.

These are the all-important ground rules or guidelines which should govern your speech behavior. They briefly outline the practices which should enable you to manage your disorder.

Concerning most of these rules later chapters in this book will give a more complete description of how to go about complying with them. So it is strongly suggested you study each chapter identified with each rule when trying to take advantage of the benefits to be derived from it.

---

[1]Findings suggest that the more a stutterer talks, the better, and the more people he talks to and the more situations he talks in, the better. (Johnson)

[2]The stutterer should be encouraged to talk as much as possible. (Brown)

[3]Saturate yourself with speech. There is a direct correlation between speaking time and fluency. (G. F. Johnson)

Working on your stuttering is challenging—conquering situations from which you have always retreated. This is because you can change what you are doing, and stuttering is something you are doing, and not something that happens to you.[1, 2]

As you change your speaking behavior, you will find that your emotional reactions will change, and when your emotional reactions change, it will be easier to change your speaking behavior. And if you can let your speech be governed by these rules, you will no longer feel that your stuttering represents a problem.

However, let's tackle the problem. How does one go about achieving these goals? Plan to go at it easily, but in an organized way with determination. You might start by systematically tackling one rule at a time. Possibly work on one which would be easy and then take the next hardest, etc. Or possibly start with the hardest, but in any case work on them gradually. The choice is yours.[3]

Also it is suggested that you set up a daily quota. The first day collect at least one instance in which you fulfill the requirements of one rule; then two in a row; then three in a series and so on. Then do your collecting as you go about your daily work and make note of your accomplishments in your workbook.

---

[1]Stuttering is a series of activities you do. (Emerick)

[2]Speech is something produced by the speaker and as such is something the speaker can modify and change. (Conture)

[3]Another philosophy of my therapy has been that by tackling situations of greater difficulty, others that were once hard become easier. (Gregory)

In defining your goals possibly set up a minimum you feel sure you can do and a maximum that may strain your motivation and yet be achieved. For example, devise the following for the rule calling for you to speak slowly and deliberately. For a minimum goal "I will talk slowly and deliberately while reading aloud to myself for five minutes"; for a maximum goal "I will use it on several phone calls whether I stutter or not". Each day record your performance honestly, and try to cover all of the rules and each subsequent day gradually increase your quota.

It would help to set up a system to reward yourself. Find something you'd like to do such as reading a magazine for an hour, watching TV or eating a snack, etc., and let yourself do it only after you have accomplished a specific goal. Alternately, you might allow yourself to buy something you really need or want after you have done so many assignments.

It may be quite difficult for you to comply with some of these guidelines since you may be changing habits which you have had for years.[1] If sometimes you try and fail on some of them, do not get disheartened. Other stutterers have met difficulties and conquered them. Give it time. If you can only reduce the tension and severity of your struggle behavior by learning to stutter easily and openly you will have made a lot of progress toward your goal.

---

[1]Adult stutterers have taken many years to develop their speech problem and their reactions to and emotions regarding it. This type of behavioral-emotional complex will not be changed overnight, and we believe the stutterer should be prepared for moments, hours and days of difficulty. We said prepared, and not excused. (Conture)

The following chapters will discuss most of the recommended procedures and how they can have an impact on your stuttering and the ease with which you can speak.

When you go into therapy, when you begin to modify your speech pattern, go full tilt, reach for the home run ...Quit feeling sorry for yourself. (Emerick)

As a speech pathologist working with adult stutterers I have found that the most important factors that determine progress are (1) that the stutterer have a goal that requires better speech, and (2) that he form the habit of working consistently and steadily to accomplish his purpose. *(Gregory)*

Rule (1)
Talking Slowly and Deliberately

The first rule or guideline calls for you to build a habit of talking slowly and deliberately, whether or not you stutter. This is recommended for a couple of reasons. First, it induces a manner of talking which is generally respected and admired and secondly, it will result in a more varied, relaxed manner of speaking which is more responsive to therapy controlled procedures.

Temporarily accepting your role as a stutterer, resolve to make a special effort to talk slowly and deliberately all the time, varying your rate and loudness. This will not be easy to do if you normally speak fairly rapidly. It will take a lot of concentration to talk slowly whenever you speak.

It would help if you could spend at least five minutes a day practicing when you are alone. Possibly think of some subject about which you are informed and talk to yourself slowly and deliberately, varying the speed and loudness. Or you might read to yourself in that same way that you should use in conversation with others.

When you are with others always try to resist feelings of time pressure. At the moment you are expected to speak you may sometimes have an almost panicky feeling of haste and urgency.[1] You think that you are under "time pressure" with no time to lose, and you have

---

[1] I have always felt a great pressure to give a reply within a split second and with just the right and exact words. Other stutterers feel this, too. Isn't it silly? (Garland)

a compulsive feeling that you must speak quickly without taking the time for deliberate and relaxed expression. Do your best to resist this time pressure feeling.[1, 2]

Stutterers are also apt to fear silence when they are embarrassed. It is suggested that you might experiment with occasionally pausing when called on to speak. Pause momentarily and be silent. There is no hurry—probably you are not taking as much time as you think—take your time. Unless there is a fire, people will wait to hear what you have to say. Let them wait and don't hurry saying "hello" on the phone. Pause! Take your time.

If you have a tape recorder available, this would be an opportune time to make a recording of the way you talk, particularly if you have not yet started speaking according to the recommendations of this first rule.

Making a recording of the way you usually stutter will supply remedial information to be used in this program.[3] For example, listening to such a recording should help you discover what, if anything, would need to be done to qualify you as speaking slowly and deliberately.

---

[1]Panic, tension, and an overwhelming urgency are the hallmarks of stuttering; they are what you must overcome. Totally resist any feelings of hurry and pressure. Let 'em wait. (J. D. Williams)

[2]A basic feature of stuttering behavior is that the stutterer is under time pressure to a great extent. The stutterer has to learn how to permit pauses in his speech, to risk the fear of silence, to give himself time to catch his breath to resist the time pressure. (Sheehan)

[3]A tape recorder will prove a good investment for the stutterer. (Bluemel)

The question arises as to what may be the best way to get a recording of your stuttering. We hope you will find a way. If you have trouble talking on the phone, you might place a microphone near when you make several phone calls—at least five or possibly ten minutes of recording time would be desirable.

When you become aware that the struggling behavior you call stuttering is something you are doing as you talk and not something that magically "happens to you," you are in a very good position to begin to change what you are doing as you talk so you can talk more easily.
(D. Williams)

Rule (2)

Stuttering Easily

This most essential second rule or guideline suggests that you make a practice of stuttering easily and smoothly without forcing. It doesn't call for you to stop stuttering, but to do it easily and smoothly, sliding into the sounds of words with light, loose movements of your tongue, lips and jaw.[1]

This is sometimes referred to as gentle phonation or easy onset. With normal quiet breathing when talking this way you make a particular point of gently and slowly sliding into the beginning sounds of words (or syllables) in a relaxed manner without trying to force your way through.

One of the ways you can tell if you are struggling is to monitor the amount of air pressure in your mouth. Try not to let it build up behind your lips or tongue. Try stuttering with the lips loose and the tongue not pressing tightly against your gums or palate. Why erect a blockade in your mouth behind which the air pressure increases greatly? Stutter easily and not hard!

You could practice talking smoothly and easily by reading aloud when alone for five or ten minutes a day while working on this rule. Read in a firm voice but keep your speech movements loose and relaxed.[2] The idea is to get accustomed to using gentle light controls of your muscles of speech whether or not you stutter.

Although sometimes difficult to effect, the recommendation is also made that the stutterer practice re-

---

[1]They (referring to stutterers) must learn to move easily through words rather than recoiling from them. (Czuchna)

[2]Feel the relaxed easy movements into and out of words. (Aten)

laxation of his speech muscles. This calls for him to purposely tense himself, particularly in the mouth area. And then release or relax the tension so the difference can be felt.

It can be a problem to get yourself accustomed to this easy manner of talking. You will forget at times but should use reminders when you are working on these rules. For instance, you could put up a sign on your clock or mirror to read "Remember to easy-stutter today", or put a rubber band on your wrist so you will be continuously reminded to direct your efforts toward talking easily. You could also make a list at night of the times during the day of situations where you did or did not remember to talk as suggested.

Most all stuttering, to some extent, results from efforts to force trouble-free speech.[1] Unfortunately, the mechanism of speech is too complicated to function properly when force is applied. So if you can comply with this first rule and let yourself stutter easily your severity will be lessened and so will the frequency of your stuttering.[2]

When you are working on these rules you might make a record of your progress in your workbook. First, you could try for one successful performance, then two in a row, then three in a series, and so on, until you have been able to collect five consecutive listeners to whom you have spoken slowly in an easy smooth manner whether or not you stutter.[3]

---

[1]We struggle against ourselves trying to force speech. (Garland)

[2]It is in fact probably impossible to stutter in any way at all without excessive muscular tension in some form. (Bloodstein)

[3]Most clinicians learn that things work out better if goal-setting is structured in times of maximum and minimum goals. The maximum goal should tax the stutterer's resources or strength to the limit and yet be possible of attainment, while the minimum goal should almost certainly be expected to be achieved. (VanRiper)

This guideline by itself will not stop your stuttering, but if you can accustom yourself to effortless talking or stuttering, you will be under less stress and tension and this will make you happier about your speech.

You might be interested in a quotation by a non-stutterer from a letter written many years ago by Thomas Carlyle, the historian, to Ralph Waldo Emerson, dated November 17, 1843. He said "a stammering man is never a worthless one...It is an excess of delicacy, excess of sensibility to the presence of his fellow-creature, that makes his stammer." Even in those days they realized that sensitivity was an important factor in actuating and maintaining stuttering.

Rule (3)
Admitting That You Stutter

The third rule or therapy guideline calls for you to adopt an attitude of being willing to openly admit and not hide the fact that you are a stutterer.[1] You may ask why should you do that when you are trying to not be one.

This is because in order to make headway it is advisable that you first adopt an attitude of being willing to talk frankly to others about your problem. By so doing you will be lessening a lot of the fear of difficulty you have when talking.

As has been explained, if you are like most stutterers you are ashamed of the fact that you stutter. And as a result you try to keep others from finding out that you are a stutterer. This feeling of shame tends to build up in you a fear of having difficulty when you are called on to speak at certain times and under certain circumstances.

As stated before, fear of difficulty tends to build up tension or tightness in your speech organs, which aggravates your trouble. Unfortunately, one's speaking apparatus operates in such a delicate, complex and complicated manner that it is most difficult for it to operate under tension. So the frequency and severity of your difficulty is usually in proportion to the amount of fear and tension you have.

---

[1] You will remain a stutterer as long as you continue to pretend not to be one. (Sheehan)

To combat fear and tension—your worst enemies[1]—
it is necessary to torpedo a lot of your shame and sensitivity. The amount of energy a stutterer may spend in
hiding his disorder can be tremendous. Some devise in-
tricate strategies of avoidance and disguise, or may assume some kind of masquerade in the hope, usually a
vain one, that the listener won't recognize them as a
stutterer. This burden just makes communication more
difficult.[2]

Where does all that anxiety and worry get you? Nowhere. It only makes matters worse since it just builds
up more fear and tension. So what can or should be done
about it? Even if you are not obsessed with hiding the
fact that you stutter, it will be helpful to get rid of what
worry you have on this point.

The answer is simple but not easy. You can counteract a lot of that worry and concern by just telling people
that you are a stutterer and stop pretending that you
are a normal speaker. You should not shirk this assignment. Make occasions to freely admit to those with whom
you associate and with whom you normally talk that
you are a stutterer and be willing to discuss it with anyone.[3, 4, 5]

This will take courage on your part, but this needs
to be done to reduce your sensitivity.[6] To change the

---

[1]Many stutterers learn that their greatest enemies are fear and
tension. (Aten)

[2]No problem is solved by denying its existence. (Brown)

[3]Whenever you have an opportunity to discuss your stuttering
with someone, do it! (LaPorte)

[4]This involves telling friends and colleagues that you are a stutterer working on your speech. (Guitar-Peters)

[5]Stutterers must freely admit their problem to associates who
may not be aware of it. (Bloodstein)

[6]At some point in the therapy process the stutterer must become desensitized to his stuttering. (Kamhi)

mental approach toward your problem cannot be done easily and quickly, but the more you work at it, the more you can accomplish. It will pay off to do so. It is no disgrace to be a stutterer anyway. You may think so, but you are wrong if you do. Please don't allow your feelings to defeat your efforts.

Start on this assignment by talking with people you are close to and then later with strangers with whom you expect to have conversation. As one stutterer expressed it, "I'm letting the cat out of the bag right away. I'm telling him I'm a stutterer. I used to try to hide this because my greatest fear was having to reveal myself when I met someone. This way I take the fear out of the situation right away."

As another stutterer remarked "It took me twenty-one years before I would admit to myself, or anyone, that I stuttered. I didn't want to acknowledge that I was different. Yet that is precisely what I needed to do in order to take the first step toward forging a new and more fulfilling identity."

For example, you might say to a friend something to the effect that "you know that I am a stutterer and frankly I have been ashamed to admit it and I need to be more open and frank about my problem and may need your help." Any real friend will appreciate your frankness and will feel closer to you as a result. Besides you will find that people are interested in stuttering. Teach them about it.

Complying with this assignment will reduce your tension, and it will help you accept your stuttering as a problem with which you can cope with less shame and embarrassment. This can make a world of difference in enabling you to adopt a more healthy, wholesome and objective attitude toward your difficulty which all stutterers need so badly.

You may think it will hurt your pride to frankly tell people that you are a stutterer, but it is more likely that you will be proud of yourself for doing it. Besides there is no use spending your life pretending.[1]

Of course you can't accomplish this goal in a day or two. It will take time to make contact with people you know and carry out this recommendation. No matter how long it takes, it will help reduce your tension and fear if you cultivate an attitude of being willing to talk about your stuttering.

Can you do so? As the fellow said "it ain't easy"— and that's putting it mildly. It may be far from easy—in fact it can be tough. But this is a most beneficial step toward relieving you of much of your fear and tension.

Voluntary Stuttering

When working on this third rule it is suggested that occasionally you stutter voluntarily. Stutterers can usually get some relief from fear and tension by doing this. If you deliberately stutter, you directly attack and help to reduce the tension which is aggravating your problem by voluntarily doing that which you dread.[2]

---

[1] Your fear of stuttering is based largely on your shame and hatred of it. The fear is also based on playing the phony role of pretending your stuttering doesn't exist. (Sheehan)

[2] When the stutterer does voluntary stuttering, he can say to himself, "I am doing the thing I fear. Also I realize that I can change my speech; I can tell my speech mechanism what to do." (Gregory)

Voluntary stuttering sometimes called fake or pseudo stuttering, should take the form of easy simple repetitions or short prolongations of the first sound or syllable of a word or the word itself. It should only be done on non-feared words in a calm and relaxed manner.

Do not imitate your own pattern of stuttering but stutter easily in a different way.[1,2] Later you will be asked to study and learn about your own pattern, but it is better to stutter in an easy and relaxed way when doing it on purpose.

Whatever type of easy stuttering you decide to use you must be sure to keep it entirely voluntary as it is not advisable to let it get out of control and become involuntary. Experiment by talking slowly and deliberately with easy repetitions or prolongations that differ from your usual pattern. It will give you a sense of self-mastery when you can control the uncontrollable.

You could start when alone by reading aloud and calmly making easy repetitions or prolongations. Then later you can work it into conversations with others. Make up assignments for yourself in which you are required to stutter voluntarily.[3] For instance, go into a store and ask the clerk the cost of different items, faking blocks on some words. Make the blocks easy but obvious. Maintain good eye contact while stuttering and be sure to purposely stutter only on words you do not fear.

---

[1] Deliberately stutter! Yes, stutter on purpose in as many situations as possible, but stutter in a different way. (LaPorte)

[2] Even if he feels beforehand that he can speak without stuttering, the stutterer is encouraged to pretend or fake stuttering—but to do so in a way different from his usual manner of stuttering. (Barbara)

[3] One means of satisfying the fear of stuttering is to stutter voluntarily on nonfeared words in all kinds of situations. This has the effect of helping you reduce the pressure that you feel when you try to avoid stuttering, and of enabling you to handle your speech more effectively. (Sheehan)

Voluntary stuttering can help eliminate some of your shame and embarrassment.[1] The more you can follow through and practice doing this, the easier it will become. Aim toward the goal of being willing to stutter without becoming emotionally disturbed.[2]

Work at it for several reasons. It is one way of admitting that you are a stutterer. It is also a way of finding out how people react to stuttering and will help you realize that they are usually kind and tolerant. And it will give you the satisfaction of knowing that you have the courage to tackle your handicap in an obvious way.[3]

It would also be helpful if you could inject a little humor or even be willing to joke about your stuttering.[4]

---

[1]We took Patricia out into a variety of public situations and demonstrated that we could fake stuttering without becoming upset. Gradually she was able to do this herself, first with us along, and then alone...In this part of the treatment we saw significant changes in Patricia's attitudes. She seemed to be seeking out stuttering instead of avoiding it. (Guitar-Peters)

[2]Now I am going to ask you to do a strange thing: *to stutter on purpose.* I know it sounds weird but it works. Why? Because it helps drain away the fear (what have you got to hide if you are willing to stutter on purpose?) and it provides a lot of experience practicing the act of stuttering in a highly voluntary and purposeful manner. The more you stutter on purpose, the less you hold back; and the less you hold back, the less you stutter. (Emerick)

[3]By gradually learning to stutter on purpose and without pain (the stutterer) will lose a lot of the negative emotions that color his disorder; when this occurs, he'll find great relief. (VanRiper)

[4]Consider humor as you look at your mistakes in speaking. Many things about stuttering can be funny. (Neely)

To do this would also help reduce sensitivity. For instance, occasionally you could make some joking remark about your stuttering[1]—such as explaining that if you didn't talk you wouldn't stutter—or just say in response to some emphatic explanation, "you tell him I stutter"—or announce "there may be a brief intermission due to technical difficulties". These remarks aren't very funny, are they? Probably not to you as a stutterer, but they could be to others.

It would be just great if you could develop a sense of humor about your difficulty.[2] At the same time, do not go overboard and laughingly and fraudently pretend that your stuttering is funny, as some stutterers have done, while feeling terrible about it inside.

A stutterer's willingness to stutter, particularly in a modified way, is a very powerful psychological aspect of therapy that can lead to a most lasting and satisfying change in fluency.

---

[1]One way to make your listener feel at ease about your stuttering is to tell an occasional joke about it. (Trotter)

[2]Make fun of your stuttering and yourself. The best of all humor is self-directed. (Emerick)

Avoidance is the heart and core of stuttering. Avoidance behavior—holding back—is essential for the maintenance of stuttering behavior. Stuttering simply cannot survive a total weakening of avoidance, coupled with a concerted strengthening of approach tendencies. If there is no holding back there is no stuttering. (Sheehan)

Rule (4)

Eliminating Avoidances, Postponements and Substitutions

This particularly important guideline calls for the stutterer to make a real effort to eliminate—that means stop—any and all avoidance, substitution or postponement habits which he may have acquired to put off, hide or minimize his stuttering. It is very important for the stutterer to develop speech that is avoidance-free.

This may present more of a problem than you think since much of a stutterer's abnormal behavior may be traced to his efforts to postpone or avoid what he considers threatening situations.[1,2] Many stutterers feel they must be ready for every eventuality so they can avoid the danger of getting stuck.[3]

While temporarily affording relief, avoidances will actually increase your fears and cause you more trouble in the long run.[4] They keep it aroused until time runs out or their effectiveness wears out. Stuttering will be perpetuated by successful avoidances.

---

[1]Your pattern of stuttering behavior consists chiefly of the things you are doing to avoid stuttering. (J. D. Williams)

[2]What you call your stuttering consists mostly of the tricks, the crutches you use to cover up. (Sheehan)

[3]The stutterer believes that the most important communication in speech is to avoid stuttering at all costs (Trotter)

[4]What happens is this: The successful avoidance causes some anxiety reduction. Then, when a similar situation presents itself, the need to avoid is even stronger due to the preceding reinforcement. But now, no avoidance is possible. The conflict becomes even greater. And so several vicious circles (or rather spirals) are set into motion. (VanRiper)

Why shouldn't you avoid saying your name, or avoid answering the phone when you feel that you might stutter doing so? Or why isn't it all right to at least temporarily postpone doing something. Or why shouldn't you substitute an easier said word for one on which you might stutter. Why not?

There is one good reason for not doing these things— and it is a powerful one. The more you make a practice of avoiding, postponing or substituting, the more you will keep on using such crutches to avoid trouble and they will just reinforce your fear of stuttering. Why keep building up fear? If there is one thing the stutterer needs more than anything else, it is to reduce his fears and certainly not to reinforce them. Avoidance only makes the fear of stuttering worse.[1, 2]

There are many different avoidance tactics to which stutterers sometimes resort in their attempts to minimize or escape trouble; such as, dodging speaking situations, avoiding social contacts or talking on the phone, using secondary symptoms or exaggerated gestures, talking more rapidly, repeating words or going back to get a running start, talking in a monotone or sing-song voice, varying the pitch or intensity of the voice, affecting unnaturally aggressive behavior, acting like a clown, writing down what needs to be said, playing dumb or hard-of-hearing, etc.

Postponements include various stalling devices such as clearing the throat, swallowing, coughing, blowing the nose, putting in unnecessary words such as 'you know' or 'I mean', or 'that is', or making excessive use of in-

---

[1]Avoidance only increases fear and stuttering and must be reduced. (Czuchna)

[2]And what actually happens is that the more you cover-up and try to avoid stuttering the more you will stutter. (Barbara)

terjections like 'uh', 'er', 'well', waiting for someone to supply the word, etc. Substitutions involve using synonyms, easy words or other phrases for those on which you think you might block.[1] Or one may sneak up on a feared word from a different direction or adopt other strategies. Postponements and substitutions are variations of avoidance practices.

As has been pointed out, stuttering is what the stutterer does in trying not to stutter. So, if you could willingly and wholeheartedly adopt an attitude of not trying to cover up or avoid, it would make a world of difference in the amount of trouble you have.[2, 3]

On Eliminating Avoidances

This step will require concentrated effort as it may not be easy and you need help. It is suggested that you read, study and put to work assignments such as those listed in this next section.

How to Work on Avoidances

Conforming to this rule and eliminating all your avoidance practices may be a tough assignment, but many authorities feel that a non-avoidance attitude will give a stutterer more relief than any other therapy pro-

---

[1] In shunning difficult words the stammerer has recourse to synonyms, circumlocutions and evasions. With the adult stutterer the use of synonyms becomes a standard method of escaping the speech impediment. One stammerer says facetiously that he has learned the whole dictionary in order to have synonyms available. (Bluemel)

[2] Working on my own I set about to eliminate every last vestige of avoidance of words and situations. (Sheehan)

[3] Be determined to reduce your use of avoidances. (Moses)

cedure. So let's make an all-out effort to stop any and all avoidance habits or tricks you may have acquired to put off, hide or minimize your stuttering.[1,2]

Your first step should be to start to work on finding out to what extent, when and how you may be using avoidances, so you will know what needs to be changed. Plan to start in the morning to observe yourself carefully as you go through the day in order to discover and identify what avoidance tricks you may be using.

Study your thought and action during the day and make notes in your workbook of what you did and why you did it. Take note of what actions or lack of action were influenced by your concern about avoiding trouble. Compile this information for several days. Possibly you will be surprised at the number of times you avoid, postpone or substitute.

After compiling this information you should start to work on trying to correct all such practices. It might be too difficult to attempt to work on all of them at the same time, so a gradual approach might be better, although that's a matter of your own judgment.

---

[1]The habitual avoidance of speaking situations and feared words will get you nowhere in the long run. (Murray)

[2]Like many of you, one of the most common and debilitating characteristics of my problem was the habit of avoiding...There was almost no limit to what I would do to avoid situations in which I feared my stuttering would embarrass me. Going to a party would be an extremely tiring event because the entire evening would be spent trying to stay alert for words on which I might stutter and finding ways to avoid them. (Luper)

Anyway, pick out one avoidance habit which you know is undesirable and decide to go to work on it, making a real effort to counteract that particular habit only. Go about it in as systematic a way as possible as you will need to watch yourself for some time to make sure that it gets adequate attention so that you won't use it any more. Make notes of your accomplishments as well as your failures.[1] Such changes don't just happen, so don't let yourself become discouraged by the difficulties encountered. Persevere at the task.

For instance resolve that you will not substitute words.[2, 3] To do this you will have to watch yourself carefully because you may be doing this frequently. One way to approach a substitution problem is to deliberately use words on which you would expect to stutter. Say what you have to say and if you stutter, still persevere.

---

[1]Make a list of all your avoidances: What types do you use (starters, delaying tactics, etc.)? When, in what context do you use them? How frequently do you resort to evasion? In other words, prepare an avoidance inventory. Then, systematically vary and exaggerate each one; use the avoidances when you don't need to in a highly voluntary manner. Finally, when you find yourself using an avoidance involuntarily, invoke a self-penalty; for example, if you avoid the word "chocolate," you must then use that word several times immediately thereafter. One of the best penalties is to explain to the listener the avoidance you have just used and why you should resist such evasions. (Emerick)

[2]The author knows from his own past experience as a severe stutterer and from his dealings with many other stutterers, that it is better to have a five-minute blocking than to avoid a word successfully. We never conquer fear by running away; we only increase it. (VanRiper)

[3]The thing that discouraged me most was the realization that I could no longer detour around a difficult bugaboo word with the substitution of a clever synonym. (Wedberg)

Or for instance, there is no advantage in pretending not to hear when someone speaks to you—nor should one stand mute pretending to think of an answer—nor say that you do not know when you do know.[1] Nor should one dodge speaking situations—or avoid social responsibilities—or give up speech attempts or leave the scene of approaching trouble.[2]

One approach would be for you to make a point of talking more in feared situations. Possibly search out one feared situation every day and go into it, being sure to watch out that you do not back down and dodge the situation after you have determined to follow through. Then write out a description of the experience.

This does not mean that you need to volunteer to make speeches before an audience, but you will feel better about yourself when you deliberately enter more speaking situations.[3] As you progress, you will be encouraged to participate in situations that offer a challenge. You need to talk as much as possible.[4,5] Sooner or later you will have to stop running away. Now is a good time to stand and fight.

---

[1] You sometimes create the impression of aloofness or unfriendliness, or stupidity when you are in reality, friendly and well-informed. (Johnson)

[2] At times you may totally avoid stuttering by choosing to be absent, by withdrawing from a speaking situation, or while speaking you may substitute a non-feared word (one on which you do not expect to stutter) for a feared one. This allows you to escape for the moment, but increases the worry about future situations. (J. D. Williams)

[3] Enter more speaking situations. (D. Williams)

[4] One way of reducing your fear is by increasing the amount of speaking you do, particularly in situations that you customarily avoid. (Trotter)

[5] Search for those words and situations that are beginning to bug you rather than hiding them until they build up giant fears. (Luper)

Actually, you will feel a sense of achievement by voluntarily seeking out feared words and entering difficult situations. The less you avoid, the more confidence you will have in yourself as a respectable and worthy person. In the give and take of normal life you should not back down but speak up.[1]

Using the Telephone

Did the phone just now ring? Don't push others away so you can answer it, but if you would normally be the logical person to take the call, do so. That may be tackling your biggest bugaboo.[2] Perhaps you say to yourself that it's too much and you just can't do it. Even if you are not trying to overcome your stuttering, you can not expect to go through life always avoiding the telephone. Sooner or later you'll have to pick up that receiver and talk, and the longer you put it off, the harder it will be.

On the other hand possibly it doesn't particularly bother you to talk on the phone but you have other problems. Let's assume that you did answer that call just now when the phone rang and you talked to the person at the other end of the line. During the conversation did you come to a word on which you expected to stutter and then did you think of another way of saying it to avoid trouble on that word? Possibly you did. If so, you added another brick to the wall of your fear.

Incidentally, when you saw so-and-so the other day and you were afraid you might stutter talking to him, what did you do? How did you get around speaking to

---

[1]The habitual avoidance of speaking situations and feared words will get you nowhere in the long run. (Murray)

[2]I remember well how often I "played-deaf" when the telephone would ring. Sometimes, unfortunately, I might be standing not more than a few feet from the ringing telephone and my protestations regarding "answer the telephone" would be of no avail. (Adler)

him? Did you cross to the other side of the room or did you hide from him—or did you just clam up? Unfortunately we do not know what sort of contacts or meetings you avoid.

As we said before when you run into normal situations when you would like to talk, make a point of taking advantage of them and speak up.[1, 2] Your opinions need to be heard as well as those of the next person and use whatever words that come to you. Plan to express your thoughts without making substitutions or revisions to avoid stuttering.[3] If you have the determination to tackle your problems in this way, you will build confidence in yourself.

As you have had the habit of planning how to avoid trouble, now spend time planning how not to avoid trouble. At times you may fail to follow through but if you do, you should make up for such failures by entering other or similar situations in which you are afraid you might stutter.[4] No one wins all the time but one can always recoup. In any case be honest with yourself regarding any such assignments.[5] If you alibi you are kidding no one but yourself.

---

[1]One of the things we were forced to do to reduce our avoidances was to make ourselves talk more, especially in feared situations. (Murray)

[2]One way of reducing your fear is by increasing the amount of speaking you do, particularly in situations that you customarily avoid. (Trotter)

[3]Search for those words and situations that are beginning to bug you rather than hiding them until they build up giant fears. (Luper)

[4]Deliberately enter previously feared situations. (Moses)

[5]We never conquer fear by running away from it; we only increase it. (VanRiper)

Here's an account of what one stutterer did in trying to reduce the avoidances that constantly reinforced his fears, as he tells it.

"For years I've been using every imaginable trick I could think of to keep from stuttering or to hide it when it came. Most of the time I can get away with it, but even so I live with the fear that sooner or later I will be unmasked and I usually am. But the worst of it is the constant vigilance I've got to keep, the constant sizing up of situations and sentences for signs of approaching trouble. It's like walking through a jungle alone. And I get so tired of always having to get ready to duck and dodge and cover up this constant fear.

"Anyway today, thoroughly fed up, I decided to attack the situation head-on. I began by going to a cafe for breakfast rather than the cafeteria where I've always gone so I wouldn't have to talk. I walked past the cafe three times before getting up enough courage to walk in, but I finally did.

"I found myself rehearsing my order, changing my selections so I might not stutter, but I was so disgusted with my weakness that when the waitress came I just blurted out "b-b-b-bacon and eggs!" and stuttered on purpose on bacon. I looked at her and she didn't bat an eye. Just asked me if I wanted coffee and I said again "b-b-b-bacon and eggs and coffee." I can't tell you how good I felt. For once I hadn't been a coward. If they don't like it, they can lump it! I felt strong, not weak and I sure enjoyed the bacon and eggs.

"After breakfast I was feeling so good about myself that I decided to tackle the phone which has always been my most feared situation. I wanted to find out when the buses left for Trenton, and ordinarily I might have gone to the bus station rather than phone. That phone fear is terrible and I hung up twice when they answered before saying a word. I was in such a panic I hardly knew what I wanted to say even if I could have started.

"So I sat down, smoked a cigarette, and wrote out the words "When do the buses leave for Trenton this afternoon?", put the mirror by the phone so I could see myself, dialed the number and then said it word by word. I stuttered though not as much as I'd expected, and I had to say it twice because the clerk didn't understand the first time but I got the information I needed. Felt all drained out afterwards but also triumphant. I'll lick this damned thing yet."

So can you.[1]

---

[1] Keep in mind that...the less you avoid words and situations, the less you will stutter in the long run. (J. D. Williams)

Rule (5)

Eliminating Secondary Symptoms

The fifth rule or guideline suggests that the stutterer eliminate—that is stop doing—any secondary behaviors or associated habits which he may exhibit when stuttering or in trying to avoid difficulty.[1] Possibly you have no such irregular behaviors, although most stutterers do.

This rule does not apply to the abnormal activity of your speech muscles or mechanism which is covered under rule (7). It refers to other noticeable, unnecessary or accessory body movements which may characterize the particular pattern of your stuttering.

They are what speech pathologists call secondary symptoms and refer to actions which are not necessary for the production of speech. These include movements such as eye blinks, closings or fixations, nostril or facial grimaces, or mouth protrusions or postures, covering your mouth with your hand, head movements or scratching, jaw jerks, ear pulling, finger snapping or tapping, coin jingling, knee slapping, foot tapping or shuffling, arm swinging, hand movements or what have you.[2]

---

[1] I feel that the stutterer's first task in speech correction is to learn to stop the physical struggle with which he has formerly met his speech blocks. (Bluemel)

[2] John's habitual pattern consisted of a violent tilting back of his head; rolling his eyes toward the ceiling; the muscles of his neck would stand out; he would become flushed; he would twist his face in a forced grimace; attempt various starters; some head jerks in an effort to release himself from the blocks and would also accompany his stuttering with various body gestures. (Sheehan)

Such irregular movements started because at one time you thought they helped you get through a block or enabled you to hide or avoid trouble.[1] But now they may have become part of the stuttering act itself. You will be happier when you are free of any such unnecessary and unattractive actions.

Of course you could not be guilty of doing all these things, but you need to get rid of any such habits you may have. It is essential to learn how to modify and control them. But before you can tackle them, of course, you need to find out what you do.[2] This involves observing yourself when you stutter or when you are trying not to. You must be alert to do this because these habits are usually automatic and involuntary and thus you may not realize when these symptoms are occurring.

It's not easy to scrutinize yourself and become fully aware of habits which you have been using to avoid difficulty and which you have accumulated over the years. You cannot see yourself stuttering but you should be able to feel what you do. Or you can ask a member of your family, or a close friend to watch when you stutter and make notes after you have described what to look for.

You could start by picking out in advance some specific speaking situations which will occur today or tomorrow. Resolve to study yourself as carefully as possible on these occasions. Watch out for any unnecessary movements you make when stuttering or when expecting to. Disregard any normal gestures but make sure

---

[1]The job is to think and work in a positive manner. The job involves coming to realize that these head jerks, eye blinks, tongue clicks...are not helping to get those words out. They are preventing the words from being said strongly, aggressively and fluently. (Rainey)

[2]Make an inventory of speech related struggle that accompanies your stuttering. (Moses)

they are normal and not used to beat time with the speech attempt or to jerk out of your stutter.

Here's where a mirror, particularly a full-length mirror, will come in handy to help you observe yourself. If you have difficulty talking on the telephone, make some phone calls while watching yourself in the mirror.[1] Note any or all irregular movements (or postures) associated with your stuttering. Don't skip any of them. To double check make phone calls which will be particularly embarrassing and will put pressure on you. After each situation, make a list of symptoms in your workbook.[2]

You should have little trouble identifying and listing a conspicuous secondary symptom, but it may be a little more difficult to spot others. Stutterers can be unaware of behaviors which may be obvious to others. You may be surprised to find that you are doing something you would not do if you didn't stutter or expect to. So while you are working on this rule, make a point of observing yourself as carefully as possible.

(This guideline does not suggest that a stutterer should stop using any normal gestures which he has been in the habit of using to add expression or emphasis to his conversation. In fact, normal gesturing is encouraged as long as it is not timed to a beat or timing of one's speech.)

---

[1]For example, you can look at yourself in the mirror and assess what you are doing while you make a phone call likely to elicit stuttering. (Murray)

[2]Begin by listing the struggle behaviors that you use which are not part of the act of speaking. You will seek to eliminate these behaviors by increasing your awareness of them and separating them from your attempts to talk. (Moses)

On Eliminating Secondary Symptoms

See next section where a systematic procedure is outlined describing how to effectively work on eliminating secondary symptoms. Getting rid of any you may have should be a definite goal. In doing this you will be getting rid of crutches which may have originally helped you get the word out but which can give no permanent relief.

How to Work on Secondary Symptoms

How do you go about eliminating such behavior. It may not be easy. Sometimes such a habit can be so compulsive that it's almost impossible to stop.[1] But you can stop it if you make up your mind to do so. You can't stop stuttering by willpower, but if you are determined, you can get rid of secondary symptoms by disciplining yourself to do so. But one needs to go about it in a systematic manner.

Unfortunately, there are no universal secondary symptoms which are common to all stutterers. You might blink your eyes, swing your arms, protrude your lips, jingle your coins, blow your nose, or make some kind of timing movement, etc. It could be anything. Also the problems of others may be different from yours, but that is not important since they will just be used as examples and the principles of correction outlined should apply to all such stuttering habits or tricks.

Anyway, let's start by selecting some movement you make which you would like to correct. Even if there is more than one, it is better to work on only one at a time.

One way to start bringing it under control is to con-

---

[1] Get rid of these artificial devices! This may seem impossible at first, but depend on your own natural resources and you will find that in the final analysis you will be greatly rewarded. (Barbara)

sciously make such movements purposely while not talking. For instance, if you have the habit of swinging your arm in trying to talk, then it is suggested that every once in a while you swing your arm intentionally while alone and not talking. And then start talking to yourself and swinging your arm but varying its speed and action so you can feel yourself consciously doing it in a different way.[1]

Likewise, if you have the habit of blinking your eyes, do it purposely in your accustomed manner when alone and not talking. And then, when talking to yourself, consciously and purposely vary the timing or speed of the blink. This approach to such problems is called 'massed practice'. It calls for such things to be done purposely in a concentrated manner. Bringing such a habit under conscious control will make it easier to manage or restrain.

Practice taking over control in anxiety producing situations until you know you are the master and can skip it altogether. The basic idea is to make the behavior voluntary while it is occurring—then to vary it voluntarily—then to curtail its duration—then to stutter on the word without it. You can stop these mannerisms if you are determined to do so.

As an example you might be interested in how one stutterer eliminated a rather grotesque secondary symption of head jerking. This is how he did it.

"I'd always hated my head jerking. Looked awful, I know, and it bothered other people but I'd never been

---

[1]Set up a program of change. Take all the different elements that make up your stuttering pattern, e.g. head jerks, eye blinks, etc. The consciously and deliberately attempt to add (exaggerate), vary (instead of jerking your head to the right, jerk it to the left) and drop out the separate parts one at a time. Break up the stereotyped nature of how you go about doing your stuttering. (Emerick)

able to control it until now. It just seemed to take off when I blocked hard. I suffered from it for many years but it's gone now. I've learned how to keep it out and now my fear of stuttering has gone way down and I'm not stuttering much.

"Here's how I did it. It was suggested that I watch myself in the mirror when making phone calls. At first I could not bear to look at my jerking in the mirror but kept at it and finally got curious about it. So I studied it. I found that I jerked it suddenly and always to the right side. It occurred only after I tensed my jaw and neck greatly and only after a series of fast repetitions. Why did I always have to let it jerk to the right? What happened just before the jerk? I noticed that I also squinted one eye (the right one) just before it happened. I found that on my easier blockings my eye didn't squint.

"Well, then I began to change these things. I made more phone calls and tried to jerk my head in the same way but on words I wasn't afraid of, and more slowly and on purpose. Then when the real head-jerking occurred, I tried jerking it to the left or moving my head and jaw slowly rather than swiftly. I found I could change and control it and when I did, I didn't feel helpless. I got so I could change the involuntary jerk into a voluntary one.

"Then I was no longer a slave to the habit but the master. Also by slowing down the repetitions that preceded it I discovered that I could prevent it from happening. There was one other thing that I did too that helped greatly. I experimented with relaxing my jaw and neck when beginning to stutter. Couldn't always do it, but when I did I found I could keep my head steady and in control. What a relief! I've got a long way to go but at least when I stutter I'm no longer that abnormal monster I once was."

Another stutterer had a habit of tapping his foot when he stuttered, sort of beating time to the word or syllable.[1] To find out how bad it was and exactly what he was doing, the suggestion was made that he pick out some speaking situations and count the number of times he tapped his foot when stuttering. It was most difficult for him to do this but he finally was able to get a count and discovered that they usually came on certain words or sounds when he was under stress.

Then he experimented with over-tapping more than he ordinarily would. He also practiced tapping purposely when he did not stutter, although he had to be particularly careful to be sure it was done voluntarily. The idea, of course, was to bring his compulsive tapping under conscious control. Then he worked on varying the way he tapped when he was stuttering by doing it differently than he ordinarily would. He would plan ahead of time how he would vary it so that he could have the feeling of it being under his control.

Do you get the idea? In order to work on eliminating a secondary symptom it is important to investigate it down to the smallest detail, since you need to understand what you are doing before you can expect to win the battle against any such habit.[2] As you gain this knowledge then start to vary your behavior. It is always

---

[1]To me syllable-tapping was an old story that had no happy ending. I had tried it in junior high and high school, using an ordinary lead pencil. Vividly I recall my embarrassment when I pressed too hard and the pencil lead flew high in the air, to everyone's amusement but mine. After that I tapped for awhile on the eraser end, then gave it up completely, so I thought. But finger-tapping remained a part of my instrumental stuttering pattern for many ensuing years. (Sheehan)

[2]The mannerism should be closely observed in the mirror, studied, analyzed, imitated, practiced and deliberately modified. (Johnson)

helpful to purposely act out your symptom (whatever it may be) when you are not stuttering.

The key to eliminating it is to get it under conscious control from an involuntary movement to a voluntary movement. If you forget and find that you are not in control then start over again. As you talk, voluntarily vary the way you do it on purpose. Practice taking over control in anxiety producing situations until you know you are the master and can skip it altogether.

The basic idea is to make the behavior voluntary while it is occurring—then to vary it voluntarily—then to curtail its duration—then to stutter on the word without it. You can stop these mannerisms if you are determined to do so.

Pay enough attention to the things you do that interfere with your normal speech, the things that you do that you call your stuttering, to understand that they are unnecessary and to change or eliminate them. (Johnson)

Rule (6)

Maintaining Eye Contact

If you are like many stutterers you do not look people squarely in the eye when you talk to them. Chances are that if you observe yourself carefully you will find that you usually avert your eyes, particularly when you are stuttering or anticipating a block. And by doing so you tend to increase any feeling of shame or embarrassment you may have about your difficulty.

Maintaining eye contact will not of itself stop your stuttering, but it will help reduce feelings of shyness or self-consciousness. It is this sensitivity which generates a lot of the tension which causes or aggravates your trouble. So this guideline calls for you to establish the habit of eye contact with whom you talk.[1,2]

This doesn't mean that you need to stare fixedly at the person to whom you are talking, but still you should look the other person squarely in the eye more or less continuously. Establish eye contact before you begin to speak and continue to do so in a natural way. Particularly do your best not to look away when you stutter or expect to.

It is possible that you already practice good eye contact but more probably you are embarrassed and do not. Remember it is difficult to observe oneself so do your best to be sincerely honest with yourself. You might ask someone with whom you converse, such as a member of

---

[1]You must acquire the ability to keep good eye contact with your listener throughout your moment of stuttering. (VanRiper)

[2]Develop eye control with your audience and create a friendly atmosphere (Barbara)

your family, to watch or find out if you shift your eyes just before or when you stutter.

Perhaps you look away because you are afraid that your listener will react with pity, rejection or impatience, which is not apt to be true. By using eye contact it will enable you to test the validity of your fears and it should put your listener more at ease. Moreover by maintaining eye contact you can demonstrate that you are accepting—not rejecting—your stuttering, as a problem to be solved.[1] When you look away, you are denying the problem.

Anyway, do your best to maintain good eye contact as a habit. You will feel better for doing so, as it will help you combat those feelings of inferiority and self-consciousness. Psychiatrists recommend its use in trying to help people who are shy and bashful. Interpersonal communication is always facilitated by eye contact, even if you don't stutter.[2] Good speakers use it naturally.

It is unnecessary to turn or hang your head in shame which may be what you are doing unconsciously when you avert your eyes. We hope you can develop a feeling of confidence that you are as good as the next person and do your best to look the world squarely in the eye.

---

[1]The value of eye contact is the effect it has on the stutterer. It almost forces him to keep the stuttering going forward through the word. It's an assertive behavior and a positive act. It's hard to withdraw and back off if you are holding eye contact. (Starbuck)

[2]Try to maintain eye contact with your listeners. Looking away severs the communication link with your audience and convinces them that you are ashamed and disgusted with the way you talk. (Moses)

How To Go About—Maintaining Eye Contact

It may be easier said than done. See recommendations in the next section on how you can go about training yourself to maintain eye contact.

How to Work on Eye Contact

Following through on this rule may represent more of a problem than you think. Many stutterers have become so shy that it is difficult for them to look anybody straight in the eye when they are stuttering. It is suggested that you double-check yourself carefully as you try the following procedures.

Start by looking at yourself in the mirror when alone and faking an easy block. Do you keep eye contact with yourself or do you avert your eyes? Try this repeatedly making sure that you don't look away. That shouldn't be too hard. Then do it when making a severe block. If you find you do not keep eye contact before and during the block, work at it until you find that you can and continue doing it.

Then make some phone calls looking at yourself in the mirror while you are having real blocks. Watch yourself until you can talk without shifting your eyes during five or more real stutterings.[1] As one stutterer remarked, "It ain't easy," but to complete this program successfully is a necessary step.

As you become more sure of yourself it will be easier for you to maintain eye contact while talking in general conversation.[2] This does not require that you stare fixedly

---

[1] Read a sentence, look up into the mirror, paraphrase the sentence while maintaining eye contact. (Adler)

[2] Be sure you don't look down or away at the moment of stuttering. Some people will look away no matter how much you try to keep contact. To succeed it is sufficient that you look at them. (Sheehan)

or glare at your listeners, but look at them in a normal natural way, and though many of them will look away continue to keep contact.

While talking to others collect one, two, and then three occasions in which you maintain good contact when and as you are stuttering. Then make it ten occasions. As some evidence that you have followed through, it is suggested you write down the names and eye colors of ten people with whom you have stuttered, or write down ten or more words on which you stuttered without losing eye contact.

Use your ingenuity in devising other pertinent assignments. Build confidence in your ability to speak with good natural eye contact on all occasions from now on, and you will feel better for doing so. It will give you satisfaction to know that you can comply with this rule and it will make you a more effective conversationalist.

Melinda didn't have this problem.[1]

---

[1]Melinda always maintained excellent eye contact. She had beautiful jet black eyes, and she kept them upon you constantly, testing, testing, testing. The intensity of her gaze increased at the moments of her stuttering. At the same time, however, she smiled, a bitter sweet smile. Not much humor in it—just a beautiful, brave girl smiling away the monsters and the ghosts. (VanRiper)

Rule (7)

Finding Out What You Do
When You Stutter

An important part of any therapy program should involve a stutterer finding out exactly what he is doing with his speech mechanism when he is having difficulty.[1] So we want you to become aware of or identify what your speech muscles are doing unnaturally when you have trouble.[2]

The more you study how you block on certain sounds or words, the more you will realize that you can find ways to move through them without struggling. In other words if you carefully analyze your faulty speech habits, the more you should be able to take advantage of controls which will modify or eliminate your unnatural or unnecessary actions.[3, 4]

Maybe you hate to even think about examining your stuttering but this information is important. And probably you have only a vague idea of how you stutter and could not duplicate your abnormalities.[5] Possibly all you know is that sometimes you speak freely and at other times you get miserably stuck.

---

[1]Perhaps the first concrete step you should take is to acquaint yourself with your stuttering behavior. (Murray)

[2]How you stutter is terribly important. (Sheehan)

[3]The better your understanding of your speech problem and of what you yourself are doing that complicates the problem, the more you can do to help yourself feel capable of dealing with it successfully. (Johnson)

[4]It is important that you learn as much as possible about how you stutter and what you do when you stutter so that you can modify the symptoms. (Boland)

[5]Early in my therapy program, I made a startling discovery. Although I had stuttered for years, I really did not know much about what I did with my speech apparatus as I stuttered. (Luper)

In any case we want you to get the feel of the actions of the muscles controlling your breath, mouth, lips and tongue so you can duplicate your stuttering and make a comparison with their action when you speak without trouble.[1]

Assignments will include studying speech muscle actions used in the formation of speech sounds and words when stuttering as compared with their specific activity when you speak without difficulty.

To find this out you will be asked to stutter on purpose, imitating your usual pattern and observing yourself in the mirror while doing it. And also to listen to and study recordings of conversations you made when you had trouble. Such assignments may seem strange and unpleasant but progress is possible if you face up to and confront your problem, no matter how distressing it may be.[2,3] Others see and hear you stutter and if they can bear with it, so can you. It isn't all that bad anyway.

---

[1] It is helpful for the stutterer to learn to analyze and identify the specific movements or lack of movements involved in his stuttering behavior. He will learn this by attending carefully to his behavior, e.g. what he is doing with his tongue, jaw and lips as he is stuttering. Then he can have a basis for comparison between what he needs to do to talk and what he is doing to interfere with that process. Most importantly, he can learn that he is doing things to interfere with talking, and hence he can learn to change them. (D. Williams)

[2] Another most important goal in your search for an ultimate cure is to acquaint yourself with your stuttering behavior. (Barbara)

[3] It is difficult to achieve a lasting change in stuttering if stutterers cannot quickly and correctly identify when they are stuttering. Unless they can do this, we think it is difficult to lastingly change stuttering. (Conture)

About—Analyzing Your Blocks

You are urged to conduct a self-examination and investigate your blocks so you can develop that feeling or sense of awareness of the movement and positions of your speech mechanism when you are stuttering.[1, 2, 3] This applies particularly to the things that you do which are unnatural and unnecessary.

(Obviously for this purpose you need to continue to stutter, so don't stop now! You need every opportunity to get that feedback from your speech behavior.)

How do you conduct this self-examination? One way to get that feeling of what is happening is to stutter extremely slowly when you block. This does not refer to talking slowly—but stuttering slowly. When you anticipate trouble, go ahead and stutter but do it in such slow motion that you have time to get the feel of exactly what you are doing wrong with your speech muscles.

Keep doing this, trying to sense what happens when you block and when making the transition to the next sound until you become aware of what is happening on those sounds which give you trouble. Make note and record those things which you find are different and unnecessary.[4]

Another way to get this information would be to re-

---

[1]Look and listen closely and discover just what it is that you are doing when you stutter. (Rainey)

[2]You've got to examine and analyze the act of speaking to see what errors you're making. What are you doing wrong that makes your speech come out as stuttering? (Starbuck)

[3]Perhaps the first concrete step you should take is to acquaint yourself with your stuttering behavior ... In order to carry this out effectively, you must first learn to keep in touch with yourself during your moments of stuttering ... Feedback of various types will assist you in this self-study endeavor. (Murray)

[4]As honestly as you can, try to observe yourself and write down your observations. (J. D. Williams)

peat your blocks when you have trouble. Be courageous and stutter on them over again. But the second time go through the block in such slow motion that you can get the feel of how your speech muscles are acting up.

Using a Mirror to Check Your Stutter

If you have trouble talking on the telephone, the use of a mirror offers you an excellent opportunity of observing what you are doing wrong when you stutter.[1, 2] Place the mirror near the phone and located so you can watch your face closely.

Then, of course make some phone calls. If you have no one you prefer to contact, you can always call stores or offices asking for information while you monitor your stuttering. Then as you talk, watch the movements of your mouth, etc., and identify specifically the irregular or unnatural movements you make with your speech muscles.

Here again, if you can make a point of stuttering slowly, it will give you a better chance of seeing what is taking place. Also, if you can, freeze your action as you block, as it would help to make any unnatural positions more obvious.[3] You need this information so you can imitate your actions.

---

[1]For example you can look at yourself in a mirror and assess what you are doing while you make a phone call likely to elicit stuttering. (Murray)

[2]Watching yourself stutter in a mirror makes you more objective and less emotional about your stuttering. (Trotter)

[3]A simple way to apply this principle in the treatment of stuttering is to have the stutterer maintain or prolong or continue any given position of the speech mechanism that may occur at any stage of what he terms stuttering. (Johnson)

When off the phone, pick out a word that gives you trouble.[1] For example it might be your name. Anyway, such a word will have a sound in it on which you frequently block.

As you observe yourself in the mirror, stutter purposely on the word, imitating the way you get stuck, making the block as realistic as possible.[2] Then repeat the block, stuttering on the sound or syllable only, but this time in extremely slow motion. It may be difficult to slow the stuttering down but keep working at it until you can do it slowly.

Now in order to make the comparison, utter the same sound again but correctly, trying to feel what happens when you produce the sound without stuttering as you look in the mirror. Say the syllable in slow motion many times until you become aware of the difference between the feel of your speech muscle activity when you block on it and when you say it fluently. Make notes of the things you do that are different, not normal, or unnecessary when you stutter.

This may appear complex but it should not be too difficult since you will probably find out that the way you stutter doesn't vary very much. You may find that your pattern of stuttering is more or less uniform and consistent since most stutterers tend to repeat the same abnormal postures or speech muscle movements each time they stutter.

---

[1]Choose some words that begin with sounds that you think of as being hard—those on which you often stutter. (Aten)

[2]It turns out that a practical way for the stutterer to observe his own stuttering behavior is simply to duplicate it on purpose, imitate it, perform it, while watching himself in the mirror. (Johnson)

Using a Tape Recorder to Help Check

This is where a tape recorder can be of service in studying the way you stutter so that you can imitate it.[1] The recorder can be a small one, and inconspicuous and its use need not be embarrassing—but even if it is evident, people would generally be interested in observing how it works.[2]

Possibly you have already made recordings of conversation when talking with friends and members of your family. It would also be desirable for you to take the recorder out and carry it around to make other recordings. If you do not want to talk with people you know, then make occasion to start conversations with strangers even if only to ask the time of day or directions while you make recordings.[3]

As previously suggested, if you have trouble talking on the phone, you should make recordings of phone conversations in front of the mirror, sometimes freezing your articulations or continuing your repetitions, etc.[4] Then, of course, after you have recorded conversations, play

---

[1] Listen to recordings of your speech. (Agnello)

[2] I would recommend the almost constant use of a tape recorder. There's nothing like being able to hear your own speech in order to judge what you do and don't like about it, and to decide what changes to make as you practice. Try to record your speech in different situations. (J. D. Williams)

[3] Another classic situation most stutterers fear is asking questions of strangers ... What I did, and have my patients do, is to stop people who are walking somewhere, or are in stores, and ask them questions concerning the time, directions, the price of some object, etc. (Adler)

[4] Listen to your own recording of this on tape and watch your performance of it in the mirror ... By listening to yourself stutter you accustom yourself to the sound of your stuttering. When you are in a real speaking situation and you hear yourself stutter, you're not as likely to panic. (Trotter)

the tapes back and listen to them.[1] Run the tapes slowly in those spots where you had trouble so you can have a better understanding of what happened.

As you repeatedly do this, mimic (silently) or pantomime the actions of your speech muscles along with the recording. You need to see and hear and be able to duplicate what you are doing when you stutter. Work at this as best you can, even if you have no recorder so you can have a much better understanding of the situation.[2]

Now that you have discovered what you are letting your speech muscles do abnormally when you stutter, you can compare their activity with what they do when you speak fluently.[3] Completing this step may take a substantial amount of time but keep at it until you feel you understand what you do incorrectly when you stutter.

Working to acquire the desired information of this step takes careful analysis but the more insight you have about your difficulty, the easier it will be to solve it.[4] To give you more explicit examples of how you can check your speech muscle activities, read the next section describing how to analyze in detail what a stutterer does with his speech mechanism when he has difficulty. This section gives specific directions on how to study the er-

---

[1]It is possible to record your speech in a communicative stressful situation, then play the tape back for the purpose of careful analysis. Painful as this may seem, it is a good way to bring yourself to grips with your problem. (Murray)

[2]In short, you need to develop a sharp sense of contrast between what you are doing that you call stuttering and what you do as you just talk easily. Use a mirror or a tape recorder to help you observe what you are doing. (D. Williams)

[3]You, as a stutterer, must study your speech patterns in order to become aware of the difference between stuttered and fluent speech. (Neely)

[4]When a moment of stuttering occurs it can be studied and its evil effects erased as much as possible. (Czuchna)

rors you make. It also describes how to work on the difficulties you may encounter in trying to say your name, provided your name happens to be Peter.

I am a stutterer. I am not like other people. I must think differently, act differently, live differently—because I stutter. Like other stutterers, like other exiles, I have known all my life a great sorrow and a great hope together, and they have made me the kind of person I am. An awkward tongue has molded my life. (Johnson)
(written when he was a young man)

How to Analyze in Detail What a Stutterer Does With His Speech Mechanism When He Has Difficulty

This section describes and demonstrates in detail how the stutterer can analyze his blocks to correct his errors.[1,2] However, unfortunately, there is no way for us to know what happens in your case. But we will list here some variations of stuttering behavior which may happen with you when certain consonant sounds are uttered. This will give you a better idea of what you can do about it.

It should first be noted that all vocal expression or speech is actually made up of separate and different sounds which are combined to make words.[3] To express it in another way, when you talk you articulate sounds which form words. In the interest of simplicity these sounds will be referred to as vowel and consonant sounds—the vowel sounds being 'a', 'e', 'i', etc., and the consonant sounds 'b', 'c', 'd', etc.

When you stutter you may think that you are blocking on a word. That is true, but more specifically you are blocking on a sound of that word or in making the transition from one sound to the next in that word. To use a simple illustration when you stutter saying b-b-b-ball you are not blocking on the word "ball" but on the

---

[1] You've got to examine and analyze the act of speaking to see what errors you are making. (Starbuck)

[2] At a time when you feel that you "are stuttering" pay very close attention to what you are doing ... You can ask yourself—precisely what are you doing? You should answer this question in descriptive detail, and when you have done this you should always ask yourself why you were doing what you were doing. (Johnson)

[3] You may think of a word as being a unit or lump of sound. Actually a word is composed of separate sounds much as a written word consists of separate letters. (Neely)

consonant sound 'b' or on the transition from 'b' to 'a'. Many stutterers find their greatest difficulty occurs in shifting from one sound to producing the next sound.

Among other possibilities you may find out that your airflow is sporadic or jerky; or you let all your air out first and then try to talk without sufficient breath; or you use some kind of starter noises or interjections; or you jam your lips shut and can't get them apart; or your tongue sticks to the roof of your mouth; or you have rapid-fire repetitions or just repeat sounds; or you have tremors in your jaw; or you have prolongation of certain sounds, etc.

It would be impossible to describe how to correct all kinds of faulty speech behavior. To attempt such an explanation would involve too many complicated procedures exceedingly difficult to explain in writing even if we did know what happens in your case.

On Saying One's Name

Let's try out your speech muscle activity on a sample consonant sound. For lack of a better example, let's assume that your name is Peter and you have particular trouble with the 'p' sound and the transition to the next sound.

(Virtually every stutterer has trouble with his own name, particularly when he is called on to identify himself to someone in authority.)

For your information the 'p' sound is called a "labial plosive." This kind of sound is correctly made by closing your lips and building up slight air pressure and then suddenly releasing the air by separating your lips quickly. Try making the sound by itself.

Anyway, now in front of your mirror, stutter badly on th 'p' sound as you say your name putting a lot of tension into it. Then stutter on it again in the same way but this time do it in extremely slow motion so you can have an opportunity to feel what your speech muscles are doing when you block. Repeat this several times.

What happened and what did you find out? Certainly you had an excessive amount of tension but where was it principally located? Perhaps there was no passage of air because your tight lips closed the airway. Or maybe you tried to say the name without sufficient breath, or your airflow was obstructed by your tongue. Stutterers do that sometimes. Obviously, you can't talk without breath flow. Or perhaps you shut off the airflow in your throat by tightening your vocal cords excessively.

Perhaps instead of attacking the 'p' sound directly, you hemmed and hawed, using various repetitive starter sounds like 'uh' or 'er' or 'well', etc. Or maybe you stalled and started again repeating a phrase. Because of the tension your speech muscles may have become temporarily frozen in a rigid position thus blocking any sound.

Possibly you had tiny vibrations in your lips or jaw— or possibly the sound came out p-p-p-p repetitively in sort of a bounce pattern like a broken record. Or maybe your lips were squeezed or protruded and set in a fast vibration or trembling called tremor.

Much more likely you blocked because you held your mouth in a fixed position. In other words you pressed your lips together so tightly on the 'p' sound that you couldn't separate them and let the air escape. You couldn't uncork your mouth because you were making such a hard tight contact. Are you doing these things?

Of course you are not doing all these things and running into all these complications, but you need to write down how and where you get blocked making the 'p' sound. You will need such a list to use as a reminder of what should be eliminated or modified.

Now still in front of your mirror say your name *without* stuttering, in extremely slow motion repeatedly to get the feel of the difference between how you stutter on it and how you say it without stuttering.

In the latter case you will observe your tension is low and that you attack the word or sound without any starter sounds or interjections. Also when speaking normally, you don't repeat anything so there's no stopping and starting—no retrials. You have no vibrations or tremors in your lips or jaw—nor do you press or jam your lips together so hard that you cannot separate them. Feel the difference.

Anyway, let's make the assumption that your difficulty with the 'p' sound occurred because you pressed or squeezed your lips together so tightly or firmly that the sound was blocked. What can or should you do to change or correct that habit?

You can correct it by loosening or softening the tension in your lips in order to keep the pressure from building up. When you start to say your name relax your lips so they feel weak and flabby—and then consciously control your movement so that they come together only very slightly as you utter the 'p' sound.[1] This is called a light contact.

---

[1]Concentrate on controlling the lip muscles so that they just barely touch and air is able to flow between them. (Starbuck)

To produce a light contact you have to control the action of your lip muscles so that they just barely touch with no pressure whatsoever. In this way you can consciously control the action of your lips so that they touch only lightly as you allow the air from your breath to flow between them.[1] Practice making light loose contacts so you can get the feel of maneuvering your lip movement through the 'p' sound.[2]

Using this as an example you should try to figure out how you can control your speech muscle action on different sounds in order to correct or change other bad speech habits which you may have acquired. Many of them are fairly simple to understand and can be modified and corrected through the application of other corrective procedures.[3]

Others are more complex but if you analyze your faulty speech habits carefully, it is reasonable to expect that you should be able to use controls which will modify or eliminate your unnatural or unnecessary actions.[4]

The more you continue to study the way you stutter on the sounds and words on which you have difficulty and then compare them with how you say them fluently, the more you will realize that you should be able to move through a block more easily without struggling.

---

[1] As you say an isolated word beginning with a 'b' or 'p' for example, concentrate on the feeling of movement as you bring your lips together and as they move to the next sound. (Neely)

[2] We must enable them to learn that it is possible to start a feared 'p' word, for example, without pressing the lips together with compulsive force. (VanRiper)

[3] You, too, can explore the unknown. When you do you may find that you push your lips too hard to jam your tongue against the roof of your mouth (Luper)

[4] The better your understanding of your speech problem, and of what you are doing to complicate the problem, the more you can do to help yourself feel capable of dealing with it successfully. (Johnson)

Results from Comparison

From this comparison you will find that you must have been making some unnecessary speech movements that represent part of your difficulty. Such movements would not be needed for the correct production of the sounds or words you are trying to say. So now that you have studied and know what these needless or superfluous actions are, you are in a position to work on eliminating them.

We wish we could specifically list what needs to be done in your case, but we are not familiar with the particular pattern of how you stutter. And unfortunately there are so many detail variations involved in the articulation of all sounds that it would be impossible to describe all of them.

Taking advantage of this information, the next chapters will explain how you can work on changing or correcting what is wrong by using block corrections. Even though it is impossible to conscientiously control all the speech actions involved, still by using these block corrections as described you will find that you do not need to stutter as you have been doing.[1] We remind you again that stuttering is something you are doing and you can vary or change what you are doing.

You can change your old stuttering response into a more appropriate one. There is no need for you to spend the rest of your life struggling with blocks and making yourself miserable. Have faith in your ability to conquer your problem.

---

[1] Once you begin to see what you are doing that makes talking difficult, you will find that much of this behavior is controllable. (Luper)

Block Corrections

As a result of your study as completed in the last chapter, presumably you now correctly understand precisely what you have been having your speech muscles do abnormally when you stuttered. From your knowledge of this valuable information, of course, the next step is to take action to modify or correct what you have been doing unnecessarily or incorrectly. How is this done?

To answer this question it is recommended that you now practice block corrections. There are three of these which are designed to show you how you can modify or correct the errors you make when you stutter. And they will enable you to cope with your fluency disruptions and the fears associated with them.

How to work each step is described in a separate chapter. The first chapter entitled "Post-Block Correction" explains in careful detail how you can modify or correct what you have done abnormally after you have experienced a block. This is most educational and should be practiced first.

The next chapter entitled "In-Block Correction" describes how best to pull out of a block which you may be experiencing. Then the last chapter entitled "Pre-Block Correction" outlines how to prepare to move smoothly through a block which is anticipated.[1] That is the goal toward which your efforts have been directed and describes the final step in this program.

---

[1]The terms post-block correction, in-block correction and pre-block correction designate to the stutterer the proper time and sequence of applying procedures which lead to better speech. (Starbuck)

The basic fact revealed by these laboratory and clinical studies was that the behavior called stuttering is extremely modifiable. It is possible for the speaker to change drastically the things that he does that he calls his stuttering. (Johnson)

Rule (8)

Post-Block Correction

CANCELLATION

This is probably one of the best single procedures that stutterers can use in learning how to stutter less severely. It is not complicated but it does make the stutterer confront and accept his stuttering.

The best time for the stutterer to use it is immediately after he has had a block, since at that time it should be easier to feel exactly what went wrong and how it can be changed.

Accordingly, it is recommended that you now put into effect the results of your findings of how you stutter by practicing post-block corrections, sometimes referred to as cancellations. Do your best to follow through on this as it offers an opportunity for immediately revising your behavior in order to correct your errors.[1]

Briefly, the post-block correction works as follows. After you stutter on a word, you are to pause momentarily to allow time for you to think back and figure out what you did wrong which caused the stutter and plan how to change or correct it. After which, in slow motion, you are to repeat the word in a slow, smooth, sliding, prolonged manner, correcting what was done wrong when you stuttered on it.

The extreme slowness is to give you time to make the corrections you need to make while saying it. Your

---

[1]You must learn how to cancel. This refers to a technique wherein you go right through your old stuttering block, then pause during which you study the block you have just had, then try the word in a different way. (VanRiper)

slow speech is to be confined to the word on which you blocked, although there may be some carry-over. You are not to talk that way generally.

In making post-block corrections you are called on to overcorrect your faulty speech muscle movements. (For example if you block in making the 't' sound with your tongue stuck to the roof of your mouth, almost reverse your action by hardly letting your tongue touch the roof of your mouth at all.)

The following section outlines the sequence of action. Study the explanation carefully to be sure that you understand exactly how the process is executed and then put it into effect when you stutter. The numbers in parentheses denote the steps in sequence.

Post-Block Correction—Sequence of Action

When you stutter on a word, the first thing you do is (1) finish saying the word on which you blocked—i.e., complete the entire word. Don't quit or use a trick to dodge it. Then (2) you have got to have the determination to pause—come to a complete stop, once the word has been uttered. The pause is to give you time to study your problem and pantomime its solution.

Despite time pressure and the feeling that you must keep going, force yourself to rest a moment.[1] Your willingness to stop will help convince yourself as well as your listener that you are determined to be in control of the situation. Furthermore resisting time pressure helps reduce tension.

After you stop, (3) try to relax the tension in your

---

[1]As soon as the stutterer is able to be fairly consistent in pausing after his moment of stuttering, we ask him next to use the pause as an opportunity to try to calm himself and to begin the next word slowly. (VanRiper)

speech mechanism, particularly in your throat. Get the feeling of your tongue lying limp in the bottom of your mouth. Let your jaw drop slightly open as if you were going to drool with your lips loose. The key is to feel the tension draining out as your breathing returns to normal.[1]

As you relax (4) think back and ask yourself what caused you to get stuck on that sound—what did you do wrong—what did you do that was abnormal.[2] In the past chapter you studied the mistakes you made when you blocked on different sounds and what you could do with your speech muscles to change or correct these errors. Using this information, think what went wrong when you stuttered and now (5) review what you can do to slowly reverse or change the errors you made on this particular sound or word.

Next (6) mentally rehearse or silently mimic how it would feel to have your mouth slowly make these corrections so as to modify your usual pattern of stuttering and move through the word.

(As you take time to study your blocking problem and plan how to deal with it, it may seem to you that the person to whom you are talking may lose interest in what you have to say. That is possible but stick to your guns and concentrate on working this post-block correction properly. Take your time as the pause needs to be long

---

[1]Thinking of and striving for increased relaxation when under stress will provide a competing response which will help you be more calm. (Gregory)

[2]When the word is completed, stop completely and analyze all of the errors you made while all of the tensions and pressures are still fresh. (Starbuck)

enough to accomplish your purpose of preparing your course of action.[1])

After determining what you need to do to correct or modify the errors you made—and after you have mentally rehearsed how it will feel to say the word again while making these corrections—then and only then—(7) repeat the word as you feel yourself making the corrections.

BUT, this time (8) articulate the sound on which you blocked in a slow motion prolonged manner. This will give you time to concentrate on feeling yourself correcting or at least changing the speech muscle errors you made when you stuttered. And by keeping your voice flowing it will enable you to make the transition to the next sound more easily.[2]

In speaking in this way please remember to overcorrect your wrong speech muscle action. Change what you usually do when you block on a sound. For instance, if it calls for a light contact press so lightly that there is little or no contact. And pay more attention to how the articulation of the words feels than how it sounds.

Although this post-block correction may seem to take a long time it should not take over a few seconds. The more you do it and become adept at it the less time it will take. The slow prolonged resonant way of working your way through the sound while keeping your voice flowing will give you plenty of time to feel yourself making the corrections you need to make.

---

[1]As stutterers begin to put these pauses into their speech following their moments of stuttering while appearing relatively unruffled and unhurried, they find much more acceptance from those with whom they are communicating than they had expected. (VanRiper)

[2]Move slowly and gently from sound to sound through the word. (Neely)

You need not be ashamed of repeating your stuttered words in this deliberate manner. The slight delay and the careful corrections will show others that you are determined to control your difficulty. Most listeners are considerate anyway and they will actually respect you for your efforts.[1] You will need plenty of opportunity to use post-block corrections and it may help some to practice them aloud when you are alone.

Persevere in using these corrections when you stutter. Their use will help you train yourself so you can move more easily through a block. They will break up the pattern of your stuttering and help you gain confidence in your ability to control your speech.

_____

As one stutterer expressed it, "this sounded easy but I found out a lot of time is necessary before you can count on saying the word the easy way". Another one commented, "it was pretty tough to stutter and then wait to try again, but it's gotten easier. I learned more about my stuttering each time I did it".

---

[1]Most people, believe it or not, would be considerate and sympathetic of your problem. (Barbara)

K-k-k-katie, beautiful Katie
You're the only g-g-g-girl that I adore
And when the m-moon shines
Over the cowshed
I'll be waiting by the k-k-k-kitchen door.

(Above are words from a favorite song published many years ago.
It would probably be more difficult to popularize such a stuttering
song now.)

Rule (8)

In-Block Correction

PULL-OUT

With the post-block correction you learned how to cancel your stuttering after it had occurred. Now it is suggested that you can use a somewhat comparable method of pulling out of a block when you are in the midst of one.[1] This is to be used in those cases where you have the need for easing out of a block with which you are struggling.[2] What do you usually do when you feel yourself stuck in a block with no warning?

Perhaps you have tried to escape from such a block by using some intelligent procedure, but more probably you just struggle blindly, trying to force your way out, which only makes things worse, or you may resort to some release gimmick which has helped you in the past. We suggest that it would be better to use a systematic method, one that is compatible with this therapy approach, called an 'in-block' correction.

Here's the way it works. When you find yourself in the middle of a block, don't pause and don't stop and try again. Instead, continue the stuttering, slowing it down and letting the block run its course, deliberately making a smooth prolongation of what you are doing.[3] In

---

[1]You must learn how to pull out of your old blocks voluntarily, to get them under voluntary control before uttering the word. (VanRiper)

[2]It is possible to release yourself voluntarily from blocking or repeating prior to completing a word utterance. (Czuchna)

[3]He (the stutterer) can change the way he stutters by deliberately "hanging on to" or prolonging the troublesome sound without struggling or unnecessary forcing. (Luper)

doing this you will be stabilizing the sound by slowing down a repetition, or changing the repetition to a prolongation, or smoothing out a tremor, or pulling out of a fixation as you ease out of the block.

In doing this you will come to realize that you can control the duration of your block by changing the rate and then learning to smooth out your stutter.[1] Anyway, hold the stuttering long enough to feel control and figure out what you are doing wrong and what needs to be done to change your faulty actions. From your previous study you should realize what you can do to counteract your incorrect speech behavior.

After you have figured this out, then voluntarily release yourself by discontinuing the prolongation or repetitions—and in slow motion put into effect the measures you decided would reverse or correct the abnormal speech muscle action.[2]

If for any reason you are unable to get hold of your stutter and move out of the block as described above, then it would be better for you to do a post-block correction in order for you to keep the feeling of being in control. In any case you should be able to correct what you did wrong because of what you have learned from your analysis and study of the way you stutter.

---

[1]As stutterers learn that they can control the duration of the stuttering block, the fear of not being able to complete the message disappears. (D. Williams)

[2]In pulling out of blocks the stutterer does not let the original blocking run its course as he does in cancellation. Instead he makes a deliberate attempt to modify it before the release occurs and before the word is spoken. (VanRiper)

Rule (8)

Pre-Block Correction

PREPARATORY SET

Presumably you have now conscientiously practiced and regularly employed post-block and in-block corrections when you stuttered. In doing this you learned new ways of responding and how to move through a block in a predetermined manner. You should now be adept at correcting your stuttering after it happens.

However, you may have felt that post-block corrections were like locking the barn door after the horse was stolen since the process did not stop the stuttering when it started. Of course you are right, but it is essential for you to have had this training because it paves the way for this next step. Obviously, you now need to learn how to make preparations to forestall your stuttering before it happens.[1] This process of controlling your blocks before they occur is called 'pre-block' correction.

Most of the time the stutterer anticipates when he may have trouble before it happens. In fact stuttering is sometimes referred to as an "anticipatory struggle reaction", which in effect says that the stutterer anticipates trouble and reacts by struggling to avoid it. Occasionally there is no anticipation and the blocks surprise you and this will be discussed later.

---

[1] You must learn how to prepare for the speech attempt on feared words so they can be spoken without interference or abnormality. (VanRiper)

Since you usually have anticipation of difficulty before it happens we propose that you take advantage of this fact. To do so will give you an opportunity to respond to the threat of trouble by preparing for it ahead of time.

So in this step it is suggested that you learn how to cope with your stuttering by moving out ahead of a block and approaching it in a new and better way through employing these pre-block corrections. They are similar to the post-block corrections except for the fact that your planning is done before (pre) rather than after (post) the need arises.

In the pre-block correction when you anticipate stuttering on a word or sound, you are to pause just before saying the word in order to plan how you will attack it. And you do not proceed to speak the word until you have thought about how you usually stutter on the sound and figure out what needs to be done to correct or modify the errors you usually make when stuttering on that sound.

Even though this course of action is similar to the post-block process, please study the following directions carefully so you will know exactly how it should be done. It is a key part of your therapy program.

To prevent any possible misunderstanding we outline in detail how these pre-block corrections should be put into action since it will require concentration on your part. The numbers in parentheses refer to the steps in the procedure.

Pre-Block Correction—Sequence of Action

This is the exact procedure you should follow in using a pre-block correction when you approach a feared sound or word. Just as you come up to the word and before you start to say it, (1) pause—come to a complete stop. This pause before starting to say the word gives you time to calm yourself and to plan and rehearse how you will deal with the word.

This pause may cause some embarrassment, but again you have got to have the courage to follow through on this. Others have done it; you can too. The pause will not be long and a willingness to halt will convince both you as well as your listener that you are determined to be in control of the situation.[1] Even if it takes longer the pause may be less embarrassing than your stuttering, particularly if you blunder into it blindly.

After you have stopped, (2) try to relax the tensed area of your speech mechanism including your throat. Try to get a feeling of your tongue lying limp in the bottom of your mouth with your jaw slightly open as if you were going to drool with your lips loose. See if you can get a feeling of looseness in that area.

As you relax, think back and (3) recall what you usually do abnormally when you block on that sound. What errors do you usually make when you stutter on it? You should remember these errors from the analysis and study you made of your speech muscle activity and from your experience in making post-block corrections.

Then from this review of the errors you usually make (4) figure out what corrections you had learned you could put into effect to change what you usually did wrong when you stuttered on that sound in order to help you eliminate or modify the abnormalities you make when you block on it.

Then (5) rehearse in your mind, or actually pantomime how it would feel in your mouth to put these cor-

---

[1] Society in general rewards the person who obviously confronts and attempts to deal with his stuttering. (Stromsta)

rections into effect saying the whole word in a slow motion deliberately prolonged manner, shifting slowly from one sound to the next. This means you are to mentally rehearse or pantomime how you will act out these changes to eliminate the errors you usually make on that sound.[1]

As your breathing returns to normal—and not before—(6) say the word making the corrections as you rehearsed them. BUT (7) articulate the sound and word in a sliding resonant prolonged manner, exaggerating the corrections, paying more attention to how the word feels than how it sounds.[2] Although the slow articulation may carry over to the following few words you should not talk that way otherwise.

A problem is often encountered in making the transition from the consonant sound to the vowel sound which follows. The slow prolonged manner of keeping the sounds flowing, as you utter the feared word, is designed to make that transition smooth.[3] Also it allows

---

[1]First, he (the stutterer) is to reduplicate in pantomime a foreshortened version of the stuttering behavior he has just experienced and, secondly, he is to rehearse again in pantomime, a modified version of that behavior. (VanRiper)

[2]Learn to be aware of the feeling of muscle action as you move through a word. (Neely)

[3]Any action that emphasizes or enhances smooth transitions from sound to sound, syllable to syllable, or word to word, will be beneficial for on-going speech. (Agnello)

you sufficient time to get the feeling of making the corrections as you slide through the sound and word.[1] As you move slowly through the word, concentrate on getting the feel of change or overcorrecting your abnormalities.

If you are embarrassed by the pause or by the drawling way you enunciate the feared word, do it anyway! This is where your determination pays off—you have no other choice. You will find that the pause will become shorter and shorter as you become more proficient at tackling your expected blocking in this new way.

Warning—under no circumstances should you use the pause as a postponement, although it may be tempting to do so. The pause should be used to prepare and rehearse your plan of action.

This pre-block correction is an important part of your therapy program. If you can move smoothly through an anticipated block you are well on your way to speaking freely and fluently. Practice pre-block corrections on both feared and nonfeared words—or on the first word of a sentence[2] but do not use them as a trick to get started. Some stutterers have pre-blocked on every word while they were learning the technique but that should not be necessary. The effect of a good pre-block carries over.

Select words on which you might block—figure out how you usually stutter on them—then determine what changes you need to make and apply them when you get to the word. Whenever you suspect trouble, put your

---

[1]These corrected words may seem prolonged and drawling. That happens as a result of the more careful and slower movements you made while saying the word. These will speed up as your skill improves. We are not after slow drawling speech, but speech with more self-controlled movements. (Starbuck)

[2]It is always good to use a pre-block on the first word of a sentence. (Starbuck)

controls into effect and pre-block. Continue this practice until you automatically feel what corrections are required for any type of block. This should give you a great feeling of knowing your stuttering is under control.

When you become so accustomed to using pre-block corrections that they are second nature to you, then you can start gradually eliminating the pause. When you anticipate trouble on a sound several words ahead, you can use the time during which you are saying the intervening words to prepare what you need to do when you reach the feared word.

Then put your speech into low gear (slow down) which will give you time to plan how you should make the necessary corrections. Then move slowly and smoothly through the word as you feel your way along.

This is your goal, and you may attain it fairly quickly, but until you have confidence in your ability to do it properly, it would be better for you first to stop and pause in order to allow yourself the time to make adequate preparations to deal with expected trouble.

As you get better at pre-block corrections you will be building confidence in your ability to control your speech so you can move through any block in a predetermined manner. You determine beforehand the movements you have to make and how you have to make them to form the sounds and say the words smoothly. It is important to follow through on this. Stuttering is something you do and you should now have learned how you can change what you have been doing.

Do You Get Discouraged?

If you are like many stutterers, sometimes you become quite discouraged while you are working on improving your speech. This could be because you are not getting better as quickly as you think you should, or because on occasion you relapse or regress and have a lot of difficulty.

The latter may occur when you are speaking more easily and you run into a particularly embarrassing situation and tense up and fail miserably. This makes you quite despondent and undermines what confidence you may have built up that you are making progress.[1,2] Unfortunately, stuttering seems to be particularly susceptible to reoccurring.[3] And it should be pointed out that there are several factors which are working against your efforts and which tend to cause or influence relapses or regression.

Relapses can occur because of one's natural tendencies to go back to using some of your old habits such as avoidances or denying your stuttering. You have begun to enjoy a certain amount of fluency and to protect that fluency one's natural instincts influence you to react as you have been accustomed to doing for many years. Little facsimilies of your old stuttering habits may appear.

---

[1]Every stutterer will have some ups and downs and the course of improvement is seldom a smooth course. (Kamhi)

[2]Despite progress there will be occasional days of poor talking for disorganizing stresses are sure to intervene. (Bluemel)

[3]The central problem of treatment is not the difficulty of bringing about fluency, but the high probability of relapse; few quick cures are likely to be durable; and in general the most reliable way to achieve a lasting reduction of stuttering is to do it slowly and gradually through a process that enlists the stutterers' comprehension of what they do when they stutter, why they do it, and how and why they are capable of altering their behavior. (Bloodstein)

129

There is no need to berate yourself when old habits reoccur. Still when this happens you should recognize them as signals to get back on the job and review your compliance with the rules. And as you take care of these little avoidance feelings or any forcings, they will go away.

One factor which may contribute to frustration is the fact that almost every stutterer's severity tends to vary from time to time. Sometimes you speak more fluently than at other times. Although this may result from different environmental conditions, it seems that such deviations may persist and therefore a breakdown is more easily triggered.

Another possible drawback to improvement sometimes occurs when a stutterer's hopes are built up prematurely. This may be when some particular rule or guideline you adopted caused you to make such rapid improvement that you became convinced it was the answer to your problem. And if confidence in that particular procedure is lessened by failure, it would tend to make the outlook more discouraging.

It is true that occasionally some one rule or corrective procedure may be a large part of the answer to a stutterer's problem.[1] Generally, though, the application of the different procedures tends to assure more steady progress.

---

[1]We are all different; what helps one stutterer may not work for another. (Garland)

Another reason a stutterer sometimes becomes discouraged is because he wants and expects perfection which is unattainable. Some stutterers feel they should be able to talk perfectly with no hesitations or stumblings whatsoever. To expect perfection tends to build up pressure which the stutterer doesn't need. Normal speakers are not perfectly fluent and your goal should be to work for easy speech with no strain.[1, 2]

Besides, it is possible that you could have better natural coordination between that part of your brain that controls your speech and the timing sequence of your speech muscle action. That is also true of other people.

But there may be more reason for this being true in your case, particularly if your stuttering started when you were quite young. As a child, you may have had more hesitations or stumblings when learning to talk than other children. And some lack of better natural coordination mentioned above could have contributed to the development of your stuttering.

As you know, coordination is a physical attribute which varies with the individual. Just as some children learn to walk earlier than others, some learn to talk more easily than others. In adults, for instance, a champion golfer has superior coordination between that part

---

[1]Don't waste your time and frustrate yourself by trying to speak with perfect fluency. (Sheehan)

[2]Lessen your demands on yourself and on others for perfect speech and total acceptance. (Barbara)

of his brain which controls his body movements and their physical action in guiding his golf clubs. In any case a goal of perfection in speech is impractical for the stutterer.[1]

Most all stutterers experience intervals of relative fluency filled with hope followed by episodes of blocking filled with despair. When relapse from fluency occurs try to learn how to identify the source of the relapse. The answer should be somewhere in this book. Check your observance of the guidelines, and whenever you talk, don't force or struggle—stutter easily.

However, we would emphasize that there is no need to feel guilty every time you stutter—that doesn't mean that you are a failure. Most stutterers get discouraged at times. Stuttering is a tough enemy and needs to be beaten down time and time again into submission.[2] Accept this fact. Therapy may sometimes be an experience in frustration, but possibly you may be able to look on its experiences as having the possibility of revealing what might or could be done to achieve better speech.

With the high probability of relapse it is difficult to bring about fluency quickly. It takes time as the most reliable way to bring about a lasting reduction of stuttering is to do it slowly and gradually.

Let's review the situation in the next chapter.

---

[1]Stutterers may be poorer than non-stutterers in coordinating the speech production processes. But despite being at the lower end of the normal distribution in coordinative ability, most stutterers are not so poor in these abilities that they cannot produce fluent speech. (Kamhi)

[2]It requires patience and a willingness to accept reoccurrences as well as remissions. (Garland)

Let's Review—What's Been Done

Let's review the situation and talk about what progress, if any, you have made. Possibly you have been reading this book just to learn more about stuttering and to find out how a therapy program works. If so, we hope you have enjoyed reading it and if so you should now have a better understanding of the ramifications of this complex problem.

But assuming you are a stutterer and have been honestly trying out the procedures outlined, you should have found out that you could change your speaking behavior by letting your speech be governed by the recommendations set by the ground rules.[1]

In starting to work this program we presume you first sincerely experimented with the therapy procedure where you talked with an easy onset in a slow, sliding prolonged manner which has alleviated the problem for some stutterers. If you used this slow, drawling manner of talking, it should have enabled you to communicate with less difficulty in situations where you might have had a lot of trouble. Although this method of talking probably helped you, we realize that normally you would not wish to talk that way.

At least experimenting with that procedure should have shown whether or not you had the necessary determination to follow through on procedures which would help you solve your problem. We hope you had that determination as without it you were not likely to have made much progress.

Then, supposedly you proceeded to work on the ground rules. It would be too much to have expected completely satisfactory observance with all their objec-

---

[1]Stuttering behavior can be changed. Even though you may have no choice as to whether or not you stutter, you do have a choice of how you stutter. (Murray)

tives. But if you followed these guidelines, you have found that you can control your difficulty, partly through modifying your feelings and attitudes toward your stuttering—and partly through modifying the abnormal actions associated with your stuttering behavior.

Okay, you started on the rules. In complying with some of them you were not told to stop your stuttering but were asked to make certain calming changes in your manner of talking.

For instance, you were first (1) urged to make a habit of talking slowly and deliberately. Then, even more importantly, (2) you were asked to stutter easily, gently and smoothly, easing into your words with light, loose movements of your tongue, lips and jaw. Also, it was suggested (10) that you try to vary your speech rate and loudness and speak with expression in a melodious manner.

All right, what happened? Do you now make a habit of always talking in a slow and deliberate manner? And do you make a point of stuttering easily, gently and smoothly—in as expressive and melodious a manner as possible? If you complied with these requests, you are talking with less tension and the frequency and severity of your difficulty must have lessened. That means you have made some progress.

But you still stutter. Then, to cut down on the fear of difficulty you experience you were asked to change certain habits which reinforced that fear. In one rule (3) you were told to quit trying to hide the fact that you were a stutterer—in fact openly admit that you were one. But even more importantly (4) you were to stop all avoidance, substitution or postponement habits you used to get around expected trouble. That was a tough one, too. And likewise (6) you were told to continually maintain good, natural eye contact when stuttering to help reduce feelings of shame.

Have you definitely changed your attitude and conduct so that you will now openly discuss your stuttering with anybody? Also, do you maintain good eye contact with your listener when having difficulty? And can it be assumed that you no longer try to avoid, postpone or substitute? If you have complied with these rules, you have eliminated much of the worry and anxiety which torments stutterers and increases their tension. Just to have decreased some of your fears should have made life more pleasant.

All of the above was primarily essential in helping you calm some of the tension and reduce some of the fears which are the basic ingredients causing or aggravating your trouble.

Under (5) you worked on finding out if you had any secondary symptoms accompanying your stuttering. And if you did, supposedly you worked hard to eliminate them—so hopefully, you are now rid of that part of your stuttering act. Accordingly, your stuttering was then confined to irregularities in the way you operated your speech mechanism.

Your next step under rule (7) was to make a careful study of your stuttering pattern. To do this it was necessary to accurately duplicate what you had your speech mechanisms do when you stuttered. Accordingly, by monitoring your speech you obtained a clear understanding of what you did irregularly or abnormally with your speech muscles (lips, tongue and jaw) which was wrong and not needed in the production of speech.

Having obtained this valuable detailed information about your wrong speech muscle actions, you were asked to modify or eliminate these wrong speech actions by employing block corrections. These key procedures (8) were not easy to work but were organized to eliminate or modify the articulatory errors which you made when stuttering.

They were designed to help you guide your speech muscle movements easily and smoothly into, through and out of your blocks by substituting new patterns for old habits. In other words they should have helped you to eliminate or modify the irregular actions which characterized your stutter.

Theoretically that eliminated your stuttering, but practically, it should have at least helped you to speak without much or all of the blocking maneuvers you previously experienced. Habits which you have learned can be unlearned.

The other rules not mentioned above were part of your program and we assume were not overlooked. One of them (9) urged that you keep your speech moving forward with no repetitions or back-tracking so as to keep continuous voicing progress.

Another (11) advocated that you pay more attention and think more about what fluency you had. You have worried about and brooded over your stuttering long enough. And if you have made a point of feeling what fluency you have, the more it should have helped you to build confidence. And obviously, it is presumed (12) that you have tried to talk as much as possible as otherwise you would not have made the opportunities you needed to work on your speech.

The above briefly summarizes the results which we hope you were able to accomplish in following the twelve rules or guidelines. Have you given it time? Where are you now? See next chapter for conclusions.

Where Are You—Conclusion

If you have done your best to comply with all these guidelines, you have completed this therapy program. We don't know how fluent you have become—possibly you have come a long way—possibly you haven't. This book only describes an approach which will work. You are the one who has produced the results.[1]

In following this program supposedly you now willingly admit that you are a stutterer and hopefully have eliminated any avoidance habits you may have had. This should have helped relieve a lot of your anxiety and helped you develop more self-confidence and increased your ability to tolerate stress.

Also if you have learned nothing else, you should have found out that you can change your way of talking.[2,3] That's for sure. And if you can vary the pattern of your stuttering, you can learn to control it. You want and need that feeling of control which enables you to talk easily and comfortably.

And if you had the patience to stick to your guns in this program we'll bet you're glad that you didn't back out. But even for those who have made rapid progress we advise caution. Strange as it may seem you may need to adjust to fluent speech.[4]

---

[1]It is not a matter of luck. You can make your own "luck". You can get there. (J. D. Williams)

[2]Speech is something produced by the speaker and as such is something the speaker can modify and change. (Conture)

[3]By learning that he has a choice in the way he talks and in the manner in which he reacts, he will come to realize that he can be responsible for the way he talks. He will come to be the kind of speaker who can change the speaking he does. (D. Williams)

[4]You may be astonished that fluency is anything to which you would have to adjust. Yet it is a central problem in the consolidation of improvement. (Sheehan)

You may need to monitor your speech as you become fluent, depending on your reactions. For instance you might start talking so fast that you do not become aware of avoidances or struggles that could develop. Furthermore since you have not been accustomed to talking freely, any inability to express yourself in managing phrases or sentences may cause you to lose confidence in your way of talking.[1]

As has been pointed out, unfortunately, stuttering seems to be particularly susceptible to reoccurring.[2] You will need to guard against slipping back into old habits. Habits which you acquired years ago and which have been performed for many years can reinstate themselves if you aren't careful. You could at times be confronted with old fears.

If you should be confronted with such fears, the most important point for you to remember is that a willingness to stutter in a modified way can be a tremendous factor toward sustaining and reinforcing your fluency.

Also to help prevent backsliding or regression be careful and do your best to make certain that your speech is governed so that you talk in accordance with the ground rules. These common sense measures can always help you communicate with less stress and strain. And be sure that you do not start avoiding.

---

[1]We have seen stutterers who have become quite fluent following therapy, but who still lack conversational skills. A typical example would be the young man who is no longer afraid to talk to a young woman, but who doesn't know what to say when he meets one. (Guitar-Peters)

[2]Traces of the disorder usually remain and relapses occur. (Freund)

If you should run into any usual difficulty you can always use block corrections. It might be well to review and practice them occasionally anyway, since you may always be able to use them to advantage.

Actually as time passes on, you should continue to gain confidence in your ability to control your speech.[1] And the more confidence you have, the more freedom from fear you will experience.

On the other hand don't expect or claim too much.[2] Don't be too anxious to talk too well too soon and don't make excessive demands on your speech which will be impossible to achieve. And don't be fooled into thinking that just because you don't stutter that that automatically makes you witty, charming and persuasive.[3]

If someone says you are cured, don't feel that you have to prove it. Instead tell him or her that you still stutter and actually show them that you can do so by stuttering voluntarily. If you always call yourself a stutterer you will be under no pressure not to be one. Remember stuttering is largely what the stutterer does trying not to stutter.

---

[1]Confidence comes when we do battle and succeed. It comes when we accept a challenge instead of running away from it. (VanRiper)

[2]On the whole people who stutter are highly intelligent and capable. Yet there appears to be a discrepancy between their realistic capabilities and potentialities and what they realistically expect of themselves ... To avoid this dilemma, make your expectations more reasonable. (Barbara)

[3]Stutterers are no better or no worse than anyone else, and you would not necessarily set the world on fire if you only did not stutter. You would just talk better. (Emerick)

Your speech, like others, doesn't have to be perfect.[1] Most people are disfluent and don't have verbal perfection—ex-stutterers or not. Stuttering is a stubborn handicap and if you have conquered it to the extent that you have freedom from fear, you can no longer claim it as a handicap. Therapy is a challenge as life is a challenge. Have faith in yourself.[2]

And if you have just been reading this book for information, we would again point out that there is no reason for you to spend the rest of your life stuttering helplessly and making yourself miserable. Others have prevailed and so can you. Program yourself for success and have confidence in your ability to achieve it.

The End

---

[1]Perfect fluency is not obtainable and is a self-defeating goal. (Sheehan)

[2]After all, fellow stutterers, there are strength and resources within each of us. Only through these can we really accomplish anything. (Brown)

Life's battles don't always go
  To the strongest or fastest man;
But sooner or later the man who wins
  Is the man who thinks he can!

Sharing Problems with Other Stutterers

Self-help therapy clubs or councils have been orga-nized in many cities where stutterers can attend regular meetings which give them the opportunity of discussing their problem with others who have the same difficulties.

The social contacts established in such groups gen-erally make one feel more relaxed and it is comforting to talk over and share experiences with others who are sym-pathetic and understanding about the troubles which confront them.

Also, in attending such group meetings it gives stut-terers a suitable and encouraging place to work on em-phasizing the modification procedures which are designed to correct their irregular or abnormal habits.

142

Appendix

Explaining to a Non-Stutterer the
Effect of Fear

If you should have occasion to explain to a non-stutterer how fear of difficulty can affect one's speech, the following illustration could be used. Assuming the non-stutterer has nothing wrong with his legs, you would point out that he should be able to walk easily without trouble or quite "fluently" along a rather long plank, twelve inches wide, when it is placed on the ground.

But if that same plank is placed on a brick wall some five or six feet above the ground, then if the non-stutterer was asked to walk along the plank, he would probably develop a fear of falling. As a result, it would be difficult for him to walk along the plank in a normal way. In fact it is probable that he would put on a poor exhibition of walking normally or "fluently."

This example is somewhat parallel to the problem of a stutterer. The stutterer has the physical equipment to talk properly, but has a fear of speech difficulty (developed from past experiences) which causes him to try to force trouble-free speech. And since smooth speech cannot be forced the result is that he does not speak "fluently."

What Causes a Child to Stutter?

This is a frustrating question because in spite of the many things we know about stuttering, we cannot provide a clear-cut answer. It is best to start our response with "We don't know, but…" It seems that children stutter for many reasons which vary from one child to the next. Stuttering sometimes continues when early causes are no longer in effect. Evidence shows that some children have basic problems managing the fine coordination and timing sequences of the movements needed for fluent speech, especially during the early years. Lack of coordination in speech may cause disfluency just as poor coordination of large muscles may cause stumbling while learning to walk. Stuttering may continue as the child learns to control speech muscles, although in some children it may fade away. This leads us to believe that some other unknown factor must account for the continued development of stuttering.

Similarly, certain kinds of emotional stress—either a single very disturbing event or a continuing pattern of stress—can disrupt speech patterns in most of us. The young child is particularly vulnerable because he is still learning to manage his emotions and many things seem threatening to him. Speech disruptions may become a symptom of inner conflict and anxiety. The child may begin to fear certain speaking situations because in his mind they are similar to others in which he has had difficulty. Not all children who undergo similar experiences begin to stutter however.

Normal disfluencies that every child has may of themselves be a source of difficulty. The child himself or those around him may react to these disfluencies in such a way that he feels compelled to eliminate them. The more he tries to do so, the worse they become, and the more unfavorably others react to them. A vicious circle begins and he is soon caught up in a way of talking that he feels he can no longer control.

You may have wondered if a child could be stuttering because of an intensely frightening experience. Although this could be the reason for some initial disruption in speech, it usually has only a temporary effect and causes stuttering in very few people. Can stuttering be "caught" through imitation? Most of the evidence leads us to conclude that it seldom if ever starts in this way.

Stuttering does tend to run in families, but does this mean it is inherited? This could indicate some kind of organic basis. Some scientists have found what seems to be a genetic basis for speech interruptions which may, in turn, develop into stuttering, but for many stutterers this factor may not be important.

You see that we cannot say, "This is why young children stutter," but we do know many of the things that make it develop into a serious problem. Some of these things concern the child himself; but others involve the parent's attitudes and behavior.

(Above is from the booklet entitled "If Your Child Stutters: A Guide for Parents" by Stanley Ainsworth, Ph.D. and Jane Fraser-Gruss—published by the Speech Foundation of America)

What is the Edinburgh Masker
and is it recommended for therapy?

The Edinburgh Masker is an electronic device designed to alleviate stuttering by generating a buzzing noise in the stutterer's ears to make it more difficult or impossible for him to hear the sound of his own voice. It works on the principle of auditory feedback masking.

A small microphone (about ¾″ in diameter) strapped to the stutterer's throat triggers an electric control box by the vibrations of the stutterer's vocal cords. The noise is transmitted by wires to earphones placed in both ears from the small control box which is about the size of a cigarette package and can be clipped to the belt or carried in a pocket.

The unit can be regulated by an on-off switch which enables the wearer to mask his voice only when he needs it. Since the wearer does not hear himself when he talks, his voice and articulation tend to become somewhat abnormal which, it is claimed, with practice can be corrected.

The Masker can be considered as a crutch for use by various stutterers. Although it cannot help some stutterers—for instance those with silent blockings—it may enable many with vocalized stutterings to speak with much less difficulty. For the latter it can serve as sort of a back-up release or reserve tool.

As used by these stutterers, it tends to give them more confidence and lessens their need for avoidance of embarrassing situations. This may result in some psychological carry-over effect when the unit is not worn.

However, generally it has little or no carry-over effect and its use in therapy is not recommended by speech pathologists except possibly in those cases where the stutterer has been unwilling or unable to make any progress with approved methods of treatment.

147

On Breath Control

Although easy quiet breathing is helpful in enabling the stutterer to speak more freely it is not suggested that the stutterer try to consciously control the inhalation and exhalation of his breath. Trying to consciously control breath can too often result in breathing abnormalities including speaking at the end of breath, gasping or hyperventilation with a resulting increase in tension.[1]

Actually as suggested in this book, the stutterer should try to speak slowly and smoothly particularly in the initiation of words in an easy onset manner with soft contacts and continuous phonation which will help to influence natural and proper breathing.

A number of years ago in an effort to create relaxed breathing it was suggested that the stutterer should make a slight "sigh" as he tackled a block with the thought that this would keep his vocal cords open and relaxed which would enable the stutterer to move through a block without trouble. This technique frequently works as it distracts the mind from fear, but as such distractive effect wears off, the stutterer may be left with abnormalities such as mentioned above.

To sum it up it takes very little breath to speak. So since breathing is more or less automatic, it should usually not be necessary for a stutterer to try to keep it under conscious control.[2]

---

[1] There are dangers in the deliberate control of the breath for speaking. (VanRiper)

[2] Breath control is best when it is automatic and not under conscious control...Breathing should be relatively automatic and unconscious so, in general, the less attention you give to it, the better. (Luper)

To You–The Stutterer

Smile and make up your mind that you are going to be happier and get more joy out of life!

As you follow the suggestions in this book, bear in mind that stuttering is your problem and yours alone, and it probably will take a lot of discipline and desire to accomplish your purpose.

Adopt a positive attitude and encourage yourself to maintain a realistic commitment to undertake the difficult assignments needed for progress.

And since you may have been stuttering for years, it may take time to achieve the success you are looking for—but it can be done and the result is worth the trouble.

Here's wishing you freedom from fear and a happier life.

Sincerely yours,

Malcolm Fraser

I can see, I can hear
I can sprightly walk —
Why do all my problems surface
When I try to talk?

Relevant and Interesting Quotations

The quotations in this section are from the writings of speech pathologists or medical doctors who have been stutterers themselves. They were not written as answers to any of the questions listed, but do represent enlightened educational comments on the topics listed.

Is stuttering inherited?

There is no organic proof of stuttering being inherited, although we do know there is a familial tendency. Stuttering does run in families more often than in those of non-stutterers. Studies have found that over 65 percent of patients who stutter show a family history of stuttering. (Barbara)

How many stutterers are there?

Few realize that almost one percent of the population stutter, that there are more than a million and a half stutterers in the United States today. That many famous people from history have had essentially the same problem, including Moses, Demosthenes, Charles Lamb, Charles Darwin, and Charles I of England. More recently George VI of England, Somerset Maugham, Marilyn Monroe, and the T. V. personalities, Garry Moore and Jack Paar have been stutterers at some time in their lives. In your speech problem you may not be as unique or as much alone as you had thought! (Sheehan)

The incidence of stuttering amounts to about 1,500,000 in this country alone, 15,000,000 in the world. It has been placed at about one percent of the general population, roughly half of them are children. Stuttering has no respect for social or economic status, religion, race or intelligence.

The problem of stuttering was recorded by the ancients. Aristotle, Hippocrates, Galen, and Celsus all theorized about the causes of stuttering and proposed remedies for its cure, among them the use of healing oils, cauterization of the tongue, and breathing exercises. World famous figures who were stutterers included Moses, Aristotle, Aesop, Demosthenes, Virgil, Charles I, Charles Lamb, Charles Darwin, and in modern times, Sir Winston Churchill, W. Somerset Maugham, and George VI. (Barbara)

Does stuttering tend to come and go?

No two stutterers perform their stuttering in exactly the same way, and any one stutterer varies somewhat in manner of performance during any given day, or hour, and from week to week and from year to year. (Barbara)

The frequency and severity of stuttering usually varies with the amount of communicative stress. Most stutterers speak fluently when alone or talking to pets or when reading in unison. A few do not. A few even stutter when they sing.

Stuttering is intermittent. Even severe stutterers often speak more words normally than in stuttered fashion. Only one of our cases, a neurotic hysterical girl whose disorder had its onset in an emotional upheaval at nineteen, stuttered consistently on every word, big or little, and even she would occasionally forget and speak fluently. The intermittency, however, makes the experience more distressful, since it is difficult to adapt to unpleasantness which comes and goes. (VanRiper)

Is the stutterer handicapped?

Your major handicap stems from the fact that you labor under the illusion that you are a handicapped person, because you believe that your stuttering is not your personal responsibility, that it is something that happens to you rather than something you do yourself. (Johnson)

Should the stutterer always try to relax?

I have found that instruction in progressive and differential muscle relaxation is valuable in helping the stutterer to reduce tension during speech. Also the stutterer's thinking of, and striving for relaxation when under stress seems to have the effect of bringing about a general relaxation of his anxiety.

I continue to learn. I have practiced relaxation procedures as one approach to modifying the muscular tension involved in stuttering and to diminishing emotional arousal during speaking. Relaxation has been generally useful when I have needed to be more calm during a crisis. (Gregory)

When is stuttering apt to get worse?

When the stutterer's morale or ego strength is high because of achievements, success or social acceptance, he will tend to stutter less. If in any given communicative situation he expects or feels communicative stress, penalties and frustrations he will stutter more.

He will stutter more if he is experiencing or anticipating anxiety, guilt and hostility. He will also stutter more if in scanning ahead he sees words or situations coming which have been associated with past experiences or stuttering.

Stutterers have more trouble talking to authority figures, to people who have become impatient or mock or suffer when listening to stuttering. Most stutterers are very vulnerable to listener loss, to interruptions, to rejections, penalty, frustration, anxiety and hostility.

The pressures then, which create more stuttering can come from within or without, from the pressures of the present, the expected agonies of the future or the miseries of the past. (VanRiper)

Why is a stutterer apt to have difficulty saying his name?

It is especially hard for a stutterer to say his name, as there is not only the problem of having to speak the name usually quickly, but one's name carries a heavy self-concept psychological load. It identifies one. It represents the whole person—all of his ideas that others have about him as well as his own self-concepts.

In addition, there is virtually no possibility of substituting another name for one's own name. Of all the words in a person's vocabulary, his name is representative of something he should know and utter with unhesitating automaticity. To do otherwise implies all sorts of possibilities, none of them associated with normality. Since most stutterers have innumerable failures trying to say their own names, their names as cue words acquire immense compulsive force. (Murray)

What kind of secondary symptoms may a stutterer exhibit?

With stammering there are countless manifestations of the speech struggle. The early symptoms may be nothing more than twitching of the face, blinking of the eyelids, or jerking of the head. With one patient there was elevation of an eyebrow, and sometimes of both eyebrows. Another patient would retract the right corner of the mouth when he began to stammer. Still another patient would protrude the tongue; he said that the tongue got stiff, then he got stiff all over. With severe stammering the jaw and head may participate in the contortion. The patient opens the mouth wider and wider with successive jerking movements, then throws the head violently backward. The arms and legs may engage in the struggle. The patient may clench the hands; he may jerk the arms; he may stamp a foot; he may writhe and twist his body. (Bluemel)

Why isn't singing used in the treatment of stuttering?

Sing-song speech has a long history in the treatment of stuttering, and many older books urged that the stutterer take singing lessons. However, singing as a therapeutic adjunct has not been successful, because singing is merely another special role that does not carry over to everyday life. Moreover, singing is no guarantee of fluency. I vividly recall trying to sing "Auld Lang Syne" while making a recording and never getting past the second word. It was an impromptu, a cappella performance at VanRiper's direction.

Even fluent singing doesn't carry over, and one can't go through life like an operatic tenor. To exchange fluent singing for stuttered speaking, or to try to, is to add a new handicap to an old one. You end up with both, or with a combination of the worst features of each. (Sheehan)

Should the stutterer be encouraged to speak up?

Since speaking is a healthy and volitional form of self-expression, the stutterer should encourage himself to "speak up" and "speak with others," not as a performance task,

154

but as a means of arriving at social communion and communication. At first this will appear embarrassing and difficult, but the more you accept your shortcomings and the less you put emphasis on your impediment, the more relaxed you will become and the greater interest will you develop in self-expression. (Barbara)

Should one be less sensitive?

During my first two years in college I began to see more clearly that a stutterer has to take responsibility for making others feel comfortable in his presence. If he can be less sensitive about his stuttering those around him will be more comfortable, this will make him more at ease, he will stutter less, and so it goes; the vicious circle will be put into reverse. Since I was doing something constructive about my speech, I could smile about difficulty more. I could even feign some voluntary disfluency. (Gregory)

What part does fear play?

All of which is a way of saying that there is no stuttering where there is no fear of stuttering. (Johnson)

Word and situation fears develop most readily when frequent difficulty is experienced on the same word or in the same situation and when the individual is very aware of having difficulty. (Luper)

Once stuttering creates fear, and this fear, more fear and more stuttering, the disorder can exist on a self-sustaining basis. It can maintain and perpetuate itself even though the original causes may long since have lost all effectiveness and importance. Predisposing or precipitating causes have little importance, once the chain reaction gets going. (Van Riper)

Should the stutterer face up to this fear?

My youth, as is the case with so many stutterers, was filled with alternate hope and despair as I hungered for some relief from my stuttering. This of course is not unique; most stutterers have had similar feelings. But have you ever asked yourself what it is that really bothers you, what it is that causes despair? Is it your stuttering or is it your fear of people's reactions to your stuttering? Isn't it the latter? Most stutterers have too much anxiety about what they think people might say or do as a result of the stuttering.

These anxieties can be lessened.

I remember well these feelings of worry, anxiety, and despair. If you can learn to dissipate some of these terrible feelings—you will be able to help yourself as many other stutterers have done.

There is one effective method you can utilize to achieve this goal. Face your fears! This advice is easy to give and admittedly difficult for many of you to take; however it is advice that has helped many stutterers and it can help you.

Somehow you must learn to desensitize yourself to the reactions of others and refuse to let people's actual or imagined responses to your stuttering continue to affect your mental health or your peace of mind.

This is easier said than done but it can be accomplished. I found that by facing my fears gradually I was able to achieve such a goal and I have known other stutterers who have "thrown" themselves into similar confrontations. Use whatever pace that best suits you but get involved, one way or another, in these confrontations with your "speech fears." There will be times when you will be unable to face the fears inherent in different situations, but persevere. Don't give up! Continue facing your fears as often as you can. Besides the peace of mind that develops, you will also become more fluent in your speech. (Adler)

What about the emotional aspects?

It is of vital importance for the stutterer to become thoroughly familiar with the emotional aspects of his affliction, for it is in this realm of behavior that he is finding difficulty in facing social situations where speech is required. Not only is the tension exhibited in the organs of speech a needless and futile struggle, but just as unreasonable are the sham battles going on within the emotional life of the stutterer, warping his perception of reality, blinding his vision with fear, blocking the potential expression of his personality, and binding him to the mast of inferiority. (Wedburg)

Look at your stutterings objectively rather than emotionally. Study them by holding on to them longer than it would have taken to stutter-out the troublesome word. Resist the impulse to get the stuttering over with quickly. Although it is difficult to become less emotional about what you do, you need to become more realistic about yourself. For awhile, you must place greater emphasis on recognizing how you talk rather than on what others think of you. (Moses)

Why is it hard to pause?

Many stutterers show a *fear of silence* and any momentary pause or cessation of sound in their own speech brings on reactions approaching panic. Perhaps because most stuttering occurs on initial syllables and the stutterer has more trouble when he starts, he learns to dread the necessity for starting. He learns to dread any period of silence in his own speech, to fear it, and to become quite intolerant of it. (Sheehan)

Should the stutterer take responsibility for his problem?

I also found, in working on my speech, that one makes many discoveries that can be applied advantageously to daily living. From the time I began therapy I have realized that I must take responsibility for my behavior and the way in which others evaluate me. In addition, I became aware of the tendency to lean on my stuttering as an excuse for not participating in some activity or for not being as successful as I might strive to be. (Gregory)

How severe can a block be?

The writer was a student at Stanford University and came home for a two week vacation and at that time was stuttering badly. As he tells it; One afternoon I was studying in my room, writing with an ink pen. I accidentally knocked the ink bottle over, and ink spilled over my papers, my book, the fresh blotter, the wood of the desk, and down onto the rug beneath. My mother, sitting in the

157

next room, heard my gasp and called to me asking what had happened. I went to the door of her room, and, as I stood there, trying to answer, I felt as though someone had grabbed me by the shoulders and was shaking me violently. My face, twisted with my struggle to break the tremor, turned red and then purple. I felt as though a gigantic balloon were stretching bigger and bigger, about to burst with a devastating force, and I had no way to protect myself from it. Just then the word "ink!" exploded out of me. That was the worst block I have ever experienced. It must have been forty or fifty seconds long. (Murray)

Has rhythmic beat been used extensively in the treatment of stuttering?

In his younger days the author attended several of these commercial stammering institutes and, from what he has read, they were typical of most of the others that exploited stutterers in the early years of this century . . . One used arm swinging, another the swaying of eyes or hands or body, the third a lalling rhythmic form of continuous utterance in which all words were joined and all consonants were slurred. (VanRiper)

What kind of job should a stutterer get?

On the whole, people who stutter are highly intelligent and capable. Yet there appears to be a discrepancy between their realistic capacities and potentialities and what they unrealistically expect of themselves. Although there are many areas of productivity through which an individual can express his capacities and earn a comfortable living, I have found that many stutterers seem to be drawn toward jobs or professions where the use of verbal communication is paramount. It is not uncommon to find people who have difficulty speaking attempting to become salesmen, lawyers, psychologists, and radio announcers. There is no serious objection to this endeavor provided the stuttering does not interfere too greatly. As a stutterer you can become successful in most jobs or occupations. (Barbara)

Isn't it better to substitute words which are easier said?

You will feel better about your speech if you reduce the number of times you substitute non-feared words for feared ones. To test this out make five telephone calls and keep an account of the number of times you substituted non-feared words for feared ones. Then make five more telephone calls in which you try to make as few substitutions as possible. You should feel better about your speech when you are not substituting words or switching phrases to avoid stuttering. You may find that your fear of stuttering is actually *more* of a problem than your stuttering. (Trotter)

Shouldn't the stutterer just avoid trouble when speaking?

Stuttering is an anticipatory, apprehensive, hypertonic avoidance reaction. Your stuttering is simply the things you do trying to avoid what you think of as stuttering, and that there is no stuttering to avoid if you do nothing to avoid it. It leads you, therefore, to wonder why, after all, you should try to keep from doing something that you may not do anyway, if you didn't try to keep from doing it. (Johnson)

_____

Above all, keep in mind that the less you struggle in your efforts not to stutter, and the less you avoid feared words and situations, the less you will stutter in the long run. (J. D. Williams)

_____

In his efforts to speak fluently, the stutterer becomes more and more fearful of being unable to cope with the intermittent stuttering that may occur. The more he struggles to avoid possible stuttering or attempts to hide or disguise his stuttering that cannot be avoided, the more he denies that he has a problem. (Czuchna)

How do you stop avoiding?

Determine to reduce your use of avoidances. Try to stutter openly and audibly. Let your stutterings be heard and seen rather than continue to conceal them by hurry and quiet. Try to keep your stuttering forward-moving and purposeful rather than postponed and half-hearted. Try to maintain eye contact with your listeners. Looking away severs the communication link with your audience and convinces them that you are ashamed and disgusted with the way that you talk. When you present yourself in an embarrassed and uncomfortable way you are more likely to receive negative audience reactions than if you stutter openly and severely. Deliberately enter previously feared situations. Judge your performance on the basis of the degree to which you approached the situation rather than on the basis of how much you stuttered or how fluent you were. Begin to recognize yourself as you are and as you want to be rather than as you think others want you to be. All of us need to be loved by, and in close contact with, other people. However, too much "human respect" makes us prisoners of what we think others want us to be. (Moses)

Can you joke about your stuttering?

Most people are somewhat tense talking to stutterers because they do not know how to react. Perhaps they believe that the stutterer is very sensitive about his problem and are afraid they will say or do something that will hurt his feelings. One way to make your listener feel at ease about your stuttering is to tell an occasional joke about it. If you are in a bad block and just can't get the word out you might say, "Well, if I don't get this word out soon we might be here all night." It's a good idea to have a healthy sense of humor about your stuttering. You might try one or two of these jokes on your friends to see if it puts them a little more at ease when talking to you. (Trotter)

One reason a person might laugh at a stutterer.

Perhaps the day shall come when I can completely forgive those who have ridiculed and imitated my stuttering. As yet I have failed to find any more excuse for this than laughing at the crippled or the blind. I believe that those who torment the stutterer do so to compensate for some weakness or shortcoming of their own. (Wedberg)

Working on introducing oneself.

Between the ages of fifteen and twenty I worked rather

intensely on my speech and gradually realized that I would need to work on situations of increasing difficulty by planning, experiencing and then planning again, etc., until I became more and more confident. For example, during my freshman year in college I worked on introducing myself. After working to keep eye contact with my listener, I worked on modifying my speech and using some voluntary disfluency when saying "I'm Hugo Gre-Gregory." By the end of the year I never avoided introducing myself or making introductions. (Gregory)

Is the stutterer inferior or neurotic?

Because you stutter, it doesn't mean that you are biologically inferior or more neurotic than the next person. Maybe a little fortification with that knowledge may help you to accept yourself as a stutterer or feel more comfortable and be open about it. (Sheehan)

Shouldn't one try for perfect fluency?

Normal speech contains disfluencies of many types. (Moses)

It is good for you to realize that much of your own hesitating and fumbling in speaking is like that of other folks. If you are like other speakers who think of themselves as stutterers, you tend to suppose that unless your speech flows as smoothly as a meadow brook, you are not talking normally. Actually, many of your disfluencies are like those of normal speakers and are so regarded by them when they hear you. (Johnson)

A perfect flow of language formulation and speech production is a rare skill. Most of us have errors in formulation and imperfections in our speech production . . . Compare what you do with what your friends do. They also repeat sounds, words and phrases, interject "uh" or stop while saying a difficult word. Therapy should lead toward acceptable, free flowing speech but not *perfect fluency*. (Boehmler)

The stutterer has a Demosthenes* complex. He makes demands on his speech and intellect which are excessive and impossible to achieve. This verbal perfectionism creates inner chaos and turmoil. The person who tends toward stuttering feels that he should always speak calmly, *never* appear ruffled and *constantly* be in control of his listener. When he speaks he demands of himself the ultimate and impossible. He feels he should be the master of his words and have a reservoir of everflowing facts and ideas. He should speak in a clear and concise manner, pause at the right time, and never run ahead of his ideas and be continually spontaneous when talking . . . To avoid this dilemma make your expectations more reasonable. (Barbara)

*Demosthenes lived in the fourth century B.C. and is considered one of the greatest orators of all time. He was such a powerful speaker that his orations rallied the citizens of Athens to oppose and defeat Alexander the Great, which significantly affected the history of ancient Greece. Supposedly, he overcame a speech defect (stuttering?) by standing on the seashore with pebbles under his tongue and shouting above the roar of the waves.

Maybe Demosthenes had the right idea?

Growing up as a severe stutterer, I would hear such stories almost daily, starting with the legend of Demosthenes' pebbles. After trying everything else, I did attempt to talk with pebbles myself once. I didn't quite believe the legend, but I felt I should leave no stones untried. I almost swallowed the pebbles and quickly resumed the search for new crutches. (Sheehan)

Should the stutterer beware of following everybody's advice?

Stuttering is a disorder which can be worsened by ill treatment. Many well-meaning but ignorant individuals, by their suggestions and reactions, have made the stuttering not only more difficult to bear but also more severe and frequent. As in all speech disorders, this one needs special understanding. (VanRiper)

For years most adult stutterers have received well meaning suggestions that have been directly or indirectly aimed at stopping the stuttering altogether. These suggestions imply miraculously quick cures and fluent speech. "Take a deep breath before a word on which you may stutter, then say it without stuttering." "Think of what you're going to say before you say it, and you won't have any trouble," etc. (Czuchna)

Every stutterer grows up with the naive advice of neighbors and casual strangers ringing uselessly in his ears. "Relax, think what you have to say, slow down, take a deep breath, did you ever try to talk with pebbles in your mouth, etc., etc."

Stuttering is a complex problem whose nature forever tempts people to offer simplistic cures. Neighbors and casual acquaintances usually do not offer advice on treating cancer or diabetes. But stuttering has a persistence along with a now-you-see-it-now-you-don't quality, so it fosters irresponsible and/or fraudulent claims for every solution. Simplistic "cures" abound, and the history of medicine is littered with them. Even intelligent people who should know better are taken in, and ensnare themselves. (Sheehan)

Shouldn't one pretend not to be a stutterer?

I learned long ago that the harder I tried to camouflage my stuttering, the more severely I stuttered. It was a vicious circle and I wanted out. So I got out! How? I stopped stuttering severely with much less effort than I once used in trying in the wrong way to stop. And the wrong ways were to try to run from it, hide from it and forget it. I made the mistake of using every trick in the book to pretend to be a normal speaker, but none of the tricks worked for long. Failures only increased, and after years of agony I finally discovered that it was finally time to make an about-face. Why try to avoid and camouflage stuttering any longer? Who was I trying to fool? I knew that I stuttered, and so did my listeners. I finally took time out to ask myself why I should continue to fight the old, destructive feelings in the wrong way. I began to look at those feelings, and as I began to accept them and my stuttering, success in speaking began. It is interesting that the old ways of struggling were so difficult to give up. It felt as though I had an angry tiger by the tail and dared not let go. (Rainey)

You've tried to cover up, to keep a pretense as a fluent speaker. You get tired of this phony role . . . You probably don't realize how much your coverup and avoidance keeps you in the vicious circle of stuttering. (Sheehan)

Should the stutterer explain his problem?

Sometimes it is helpful to explain something about your stuttering to people who are important to you. This person might be a parent, teacher, friend, employer or a fellow worker. You might explain, for example, how you like to be treated by your listener when you are stuttering. The purpose of this is to make you and the people you speak with more relaxed concerning your stuttering. If you feel that a person understands your stuttering you are likely to stutter less to that person. An open and honest attitude is healthy for all people involved. (Trotter)

A reason to become a professional stutterer.

At about this time I began my training as a speech pathologist and embarked upon a career, as my wife and children tell friends, of being a "professional stutterer." By the way, I've always noticed that when my wife tells some person "Hugo is a professional stutterer," the person looks somewhat perplexed as if to say, "Does he stutter?" or, "Why do you mention it?" The point is that we are very open about my stuttering. I found out very early that this attitude is an important ingredient in therapy. (Gregory)

Should a stutterer monitor his speech?

Your first job is to observe what you do continuously, a process you call "monitoring." If you really monitor well, you will begin to drop many of your crutches automatically. (Sheehan)

The stutterer must come to know just what he does when he approaches a feared word or situation.

You must be able to analyze your own stuttering in terms of its varying symptoms. (VanRiper)

Can one change?

"The leopard can't change its spots." If you are in the habit of thinking and saying things like that, you are likely to tell yourself also "once a stutterer always a stutterer"— you might then go on to the depressing thought that there's really no hope for you.

Or if there is, there is the wishful hope that somewhere sometime you will be lucky and find someone who will take away, or drive away, what you *have* and transform you, as though by sorcery, from the stutterer you are into the normal speaker you long to be one day.

Such wishfulness makes for dreams, particularly daydreams, about magical potions in the form of pills, or secret or mysterious methods that can work wonders. It does not encourage you to face up to the problem yourself and do something constructive about it here and now by your own efforts.

What you have learned to do that keeps you from speaking better than you do, you can unlearn. (Johnson)

How John worked on changing.

John was able to observe his talking in a mirror and listen to it on a tape recording in order to begin to ask questions about what he could do about it. He observed in detail the process of normal speaking. We sat and read together so he could observe the feeling and movement involved in talking. He then tried to duplicate the behavior involved in his stuttering behavior and to describe the difference between it and normal talking. I began to make assignments for him. These assignments were undertaken not to learn any "skill" but rather to make observations of his behavior—to learn from his own behavior. Basic to all this was the question of how one can change these ways of acting. (D. Williams)

Does recovery take long?

Recovery is going to be a long gradual process. (Murray)

If the stutterer is going to change radically his accustomed manner of stuttering, he must work persistently and diligently over a long period of time. (Johnson)

Licking the problem of stuttering, mastering your own mouth, takes time; it cannot be accomplished overnight. How long will it take you I cannot say, for no two stutterers approach the challenge in the same way or move at the same rate but all have in common a beckoning mirage luring them ahead. (Emerick)

A memorable experience.

One score and seven years ago, in a desperate attempt to cure their son's chronic speech problem, my parents spent their meager savings to send me to a commercial school for stammering. Alas, to their dismay and my deepening feeling of hopelessness, it was just another futile attempt. While I rode woefully toward home on the train, a kindly old gray-haired conductor stopped at my seat and asked my destination. I opened my mouth for the well-rehearsed "Detroit" but all that emerged was a series of muted gurgles; I pulled my abdominal muscles in hard to break the terrifying constriction in my throat—silence. Finally, the old man peered at me through his bifocals, shook his head, and with just the trace of a smile, said, "Well, young man, either express yourself or go by freight."

The conductor had shuffled on down the aisle of the rocking passenger car before the shock waves swept over me. Looking out the window at the speeding landscape through a tearful mist of anger and frustration, I felt the serreptitious glances of passengers seated nearby; a flush of crimson embarrassment crept slowly up my neck and my head throbbed with despair. Long afterwards I remembered the conductor's penetrating comment. For years I licked that and other stuttering wounds and nursed my wrath to keep it warm, dreaming that someday I would right all those unrightable wrongs. But in the end his pithy pun changed my life. The old man, incredibly, had been right. (Emerick)

Should a stutterer working his speech talk with speech timed to a rhythmic beat such as a metronome?

Rate control, tempo-regulating and timed-beating methods have always been based upon some certain remarkable facts; most stutterers (not all) as soon as they begin to speak at an even-measured syllabic pace will suddenly become completely fluent; most stutterers (not all) after demonstrating severe stuttering in speaking the words of a song, will be able to sing those same words without any stuttering at all; stutterers, when speaking in unison with some other speakers, usually again are completely fluent . . .

In this connection we would say that the use of tempo-regulating methods, despite their ability to produce immediate fluency, have not solved the problem of stuttering. The rhythm effect is often transitory. Stutterers eventually refuse to talk in singsong. They and their listeners reject syllable timed speech or the other variants as too artificial and abnormal. Little generalization occurs outside the therapy situation and relapse is almost universal. (VanRiper)

How well did King George VI of England speak in his radio broadcasts?

One of the people whose activities I followed closely was King George VI of England. I tuned in to his first Christmas broadcast with considerable excitement, because I had heard that he was a stutterer. Even though pre-recording was beginning to be available in those days, he had chosen to make his speech a live one.

I got the BBC at the right time and heard, through the static, "Ladies and Gentlemen, His Majesty, King George VI." He started without difficulty, but then his speech began to be more and more labored. He paused between words, first briefly and then the spaces grew longer. I could sense from the rhythms that a block was coming; and I held my breath waiting for it. There was one long silence, brief sounds of vocal struggle, and then quick repetitions out of which burst the word. This happened several times during that early broadcast.

In spite of his impediment, King George continued to

speak publicly. He inspired his country when it needed him most. I heard him declare war on Germany. He was so emotional he could hardly speak, and yet his message was clear.

Although he was never completely free of all traces of stuttering, King George's speech improved enormously during his reign. His speeches were carefully pruned so that he wouldn't have to say words that usually caused him to block. His final illness began to sap his strength, and he stuttered considerably in his Christmas broadcast that year. (Murray)

About how much would it cost to engage the services of a professional speech therapist — a specialist in stuttering — to help you work on your speech?

Expect to pay for what you get but be sure you get what you pay for. Professional fees vary but at present they will vary from $45 to $65 an hour and you should expect to pay a minimum of $1,000 for a course of therapy—about twenty sessions—not including follow-up. (Gregory)

Is it difficult for many stutterers to answer the phone?

It is hard for normal speakers to understand the telephone agonies that many stutterers go through. The word "hello" is not particularly hard to say, but it is hard for a stutterer to say when he answers a phone, because he knows he must get it out immediately or the person on the other end of the line will hang up.

When using the telephone, a stutterer is forced to communicate, relying on his voice alone. Whatever facial or body gestures he ordinarily depends on to help himself along are no good when he is involved in a phone call. It amuses me now to hear groups of stutterers discussing the difficulty of saying "hello" in introductions or over the telephone. Usually they have considered all sorts of dodges, such as "yes?" or "ummm?," or their own phone numbers, which sounds rather official, or their own names.

Specific word pressure and time pressure are also present in most telephone conversations. People usually make calls in order to get precise information, asking questions that require definite answers. And, of course, if the call is a long distance one, financial considerations intensify the pressure of time. On one memorable afternoon when I was twelve I took five minutes to accept a party invitation. (Murray)

Do stutterers vary in their ability to produce normal speech?

The variability in stutterers' ability to carry out speech movements is probably responsible for at least some of the breakdowns which occur in their speech. It seems likely that this variability plays a crucial role in precipitating stuttering in young children and might explain the frequent periods of remission that often occur in children. It is my belief that this variability in stutterers' speech also precipitates many of the relapses experienced by adolescent and adult stutterers.

The notion of variability in the movements associated with speech is best understood by comparing speech to other motor activities that also require precise coordinative movements, such as playing tennis, basketball, or the piano. Excluding professionals in these skills, there is a great deal of variability in most people's performance of these activities. Those with the most variability in performance often have the poorest skill. Applying the analogy to speech, those individuals with the most variable speech abilities should be the poorest in accurately coordinating the speech production processes. (Kamhi)

Is stuttering a psychological problem?

We should beware of any approach to stuttering therapy that does not take into consideration the stutterer's inner experiences. The field of stuttering should be recognized as a borderline between psychopathology and speech pathology. (Freund)

Boyhood recollections.

What I remember most acutely about my stuttering is not the strangled sound of my own voice but the impatient looks on other people's faces when I had trouble getting a word out. And if their eyes happened to reflect some of the pain and frustration I was feeling, that only made me more uneasy. There was nothing they could do to help me, and I certainly didn't want their sympathy. I was nine or ten at the time.

Like most people with a stuttering problem, I had already learned to live by my wits in a way that normally fluent people cannot begin to appreciate. Whenever I opened my mouth, I mentally glanced ahead at the sentence I wanted to say, to see if there was any word I was likely to stutter on.

For me, speaking was like riding down a highway and reading aloud from a series of billboards. I knew that to speak normally I had to keep moving forward at a steady pace. Yet every once in a while I became aware of an obstacle, like an enormous boulder, blocking the road some five or six billboards ahead of me. I knew that when I got to that particular word I would be unable to say it. I never figured out why I stuttered on one word rather than another.

Some sounds—like the "m" sound at the beginning of a word—were particularly troublesome; but, even with these, the context was all-important. A sentence might have two words beginning with "m," such as "I'll have to ask my mother." The moment I framed this sentence in my mind, I knew that I would have no trouble pronouncing "my" but that "mother" would be impossible. My usual strategy at such times was to speed up and try to crash through the obstacle. When I succeeded, the sentence came out like this: "I'll (pause for deep breath) havetoaskmymother."

This trick worked just often enough to convince some people that I stuttered because I talked too fast. But when it failed I found myself struck dumb in midsentence, unable to go forward or turn back. There were times when I got as far as the first sound in the difficult word and could do nothing but repeat it like a broken record, in the classic stutter that is imitated—usually for laughs—in books and movies. More often, I had a complete block; I would try to form the first sound in the word and something inside me would snap shut, so that if I opened my mouth nothing came out.

At that point, I usually backed up and looked for a detour. Sometimes all I had to do was find a less troublesome word that meant the same thing. For example, I might be able to get away with something like "I'll have to check with my folks." If I couldn't think of a synonym quickly enough, I had no choice but to rephrase the sentence, to try to sneak up on the difficult word from another direction; the result might come out as: "You know how mothers are, I better ask her first."

I didn't have the slightest idea why the same word should be easier to say in one context than in another, but whenever it worked out that way I felt absurd pride in my accomplishment; no one else knew that in order to speak with any fluency I had to become a kind of walking thesaurus. But the strategies of substitution and circumlocution created their own problems. The farther I strayed from the original wording of the sentence, the more I had to guard against letting subtle changes of meaning creep in.

If I wasn't careful, I could find myself saying things I didn't quite mean, just to be able to say something. In a way, my situation was not so different from that of a writer in a totalitarian country who tries to communicate under the constant threat of censorship. The fact that I carried the censor around inside my head did not make the situation any less oppressive.

(This last quotation comes from the book "Stuttering, The Disorder of Many Theories" by Gerald Jonas, published by Farrar, Straus & Giroux.)

If you know of a child three to six years of age who may be stuttering some, you might suggest to his parents that they send for our

Publication Number 11

IF YOUR CHILD STUTTERS:
A GUIDE FOR PARENTS

which supplies interesting and authoritative information about what they should do to prevent their child from becoming a confirmed stutterer.

Available from

SPEECH FOUNDATION OF AMERICA
P.O. Box 11749
Memphis, Tenn. 38111

(a non-profit charitable organization)

Glossary

Many speech pathology words or terms are listed in this glossary which are not used in the book. These are inserted for the information or education of those readers who may not be familiar with the meanings of expressions frequently used in books and articles about the therapy of stuttering, including some relating to the prevention of stuttering in very young children.

---

anticipatory reactions. The abnormal actions or movements exhibited by a stutterer when approaching a feared word; the speaking behavior of the stutterer in his attempts to try to avoid the difficulty he is expecting; feelings experienced and behavior exhibited before the overt performance of stuttering.

anxiety. In stuttering a state of apprehension or fear often pertaining to anticipations of unsatisfactory or disrupting interpersonal relationships, such as anticipation of 'difficulty' when speaking. This state of anxiety may be an integral element in the stutterer's fear of verbal difficulty.

articulation. Literally, a joining; in speech the utterance of the individual sounds of speech in connected discourse; the movements during speech of the organs that modify the stream of voiced and unvoiced breath in meaningful sounds; the speech function performed largely through movements of the mandible, lips, tongue and soft palate.

auditory feedback. The sensations produced by stimulation of the ear by one's own speech, either by air-borne or bone-conducted vibrations—to be distinguished from the tactile, kinesthetic, and possibly visual (as in a mirror) sensations which also result from speech.

avoidance. The action(s) the stutterer makes in trying to dodge stuttering or in endeavoring to avoid trouble talking. Consists of postponements, stallers, retrials, use of synonyms, circumlocutions, etc.

behavior modification. A general term for any of a variety of clinical procedures, based on learning theory and conditioning principles for changing the behavior of clients either by removing or reducing undesirable behavior or by producing desirable ones.

block (or blocking). A moment of stuttering; refers to the stuttering behavior when the stutterer gets "stuck"; what happens at the instant the speech muscles do not function normally; or to the stoppage or obstruction experienced by the stutterer in trying to talk, temporarily preventing smooth progress.

bounce. The voluntary repetition several times of the first sound or syllable of a word in an easy, effortless fashion.

cancellation. See page 117.

cluttering. Excessively rapid talking in which syllables or words are omitted or repeated and the articulation is slurred or jumbled. The tempo of the speech is generally jerky and word groups are spoken in rapid spurts, making the speech difficult to understand. This disorder is frequently confused with stuttering. The clutterer, unlike the stutterer, can usually speak normally when he speaks slowly and carefully.

conditioning. Often used as a synonym for any kind of learning, but more specifically refers to any of several procedures (see 'operant conditioning') in which one arranges for certain stimuli to occur at an appropriate time so that a particular response is made to occur either more often (acquisition) or less often (extinction). When a response that formerly occurred only rarely or not at all is 'conditioned' to occur more often, learning is assumed to have taken place, provided that the change is longlasting. It is theorized by some pathologists that all learning is a result of conditioning processes that take place either by chance or through the conscious manipulation of stimuli by others.

consonant. A conventional speech sound characterized by constriction or closure at one or more points in the breath channel; broadly, any sound in a syllable other than the vowel sound.

contact. see "light contact".

covert behavior. Concealed, disguised or kept secret as opposed to 'overt.'

delayed auditory feedback. The hearing by a speaker of his own utterance after a brief time interval, a fraction of a second; in an echo effect sometimes observed in a valley or a football stadium. This delayed auditory feedback, artificially created by a mechanical device, prolongs in a variable fashion the time for self-hearing. Sometimes used in therapy to establish a slow, prolonged pattern of speech (emphasizing proprioceptive control) which the stutterer must adopt to overcome the disruptive or punishing effect of the delayed auditory feedback.

desensitization. The process of toughening of a person to the stress in certain situations by increasing the person's ability to confront his problem with less anxiety, guilt or hostility.

developmental hesitations. The normal repetitions, prolongations or stumblings in the speech of a child learning to talk. In the natural development of speech, while learning to talk, most children's speech is marked by effortless developmental hesitations to a greater or lesser extent. Includes word and phrase repetitions and such accessory vocalizations as "um" and "uh."

diagnosogenic theory. The theory, set forth by Wendall Johnson, that "stuttering as a clinical problem, as a definite disorder, was found to occur not before being diagnosed but *after being diagnosed.*" According to this theory, the problem of stuttering arises when a listener, usually a parent, evaluates or classifies or diagnoses the child's developmental hesitations and repetitions as stuttering, and reacts to them as a consequence with concern and disapproval, and as the child senses this concern and disapproval he reacts by speaking more hesitantly and with concern of his own, and finally with the tensing and struggle involved in the effort to keep from hesitating or repeating.

differential relaxation. The lessening of tension by the stutterer of one set of muscles connected with the production of speech regardless of how tense other muscles may be.

disfluency or dysfluency. Refers to any kind of speech which is not smooth or fluent. All speakers talk disfluently at times, i.e. they hesitate or stumble in varying degree. All stutterers are disfluent but all disfluency is not stuttering. For instance 'disfluency' could describe the developmental hesitations of a child learning to talk or the arrhythmic breaks in the speech of an adult, etc. Some therapists use the term 'nonfluency.'

distraction. Diversion of the attention; filling the mind with other thoughts so that the expectancy of stuttering is kept out; keeping the anticipation of stuttering from consciousness, thus temporarily effecting release from fear of stuttering and the performance of stuttering reactions.

easy onset. Beginning sounds (or words) softly and slowly with the voicing carefully controlled with a reduced rate of movement and speech muscle tension. Usually involves light contacts and an easy ongoing controlled breath stream.

Edinburgh masker. see page **147.**

eye contact. Looking the listener in the eye while talking to him. Generally a natural, although not a constant, interaction of the speaker's eyes with the eyes of the listener.

fear. Is to the stutterer the apprehension of unpleasantness which arises when he consciously perceives situations which lead him to anticipate difficulty in talking. This anticipation of difficulty may be and often is intense. It can and sometimes does temporarily paralyze thought and action. Stuttering is usually relatively proportionate to the amount of such fear present. Stuttering fears may be of situations or persons, of sounds or words, of the telephone, etc.

feared words. This term refers to a word, or one of its sounds on which the stutterer anticipates difficulty.

feedback. The reinforcing effects of the stutterer's auditory or proprioceptive perception of his own speech. Technically the partial return of the effects of a process to its source so as to reinforce, reduce, or otherwise modify it.

fixation(s). The maintenance of an articulatory or phonatory posture for an abnormal duration; the arresting of the speech muscles in a rigid position temporarily blocking speech, a variety of stuttering behavior.

frustration tolerance. The capacity of the stutterer to resist feelings of frustration because of his inability to speak without difficulty; the ability to put up with or endure the communication handicaps resulting from not being able to talk freely.

group therapy. The counseling of and among stutterers in a group, including the use of speech within such social situations. The interchange of feelings, ideas and discussions about stuttering problems in a group gives the stutterer emotional release and helps him to develop better insight and understanding through a knowledge of how others react to their problems.

hypnotism. A state of behavior induced by a hypnotist. When hypnotized a stutterer may speak freely or more fluently than he can in his ordinary state of awareness. However, it has not been shown that suggestions made during hypnosis have any permanent effect on the stutterer's ordinary speech behavior.

hysterical stuttering. Stuttering, usually temporary, resulting from acute excitement or the result of shock or neurotic need.

in-block correction. see page 123.

inhibition. Restraint on one's ability to act by either conscious or subconscious processes; the partial checking or complete blocking of one impulse or mental process by another nearly simultaneous impulse or mental process. The fear of stuttering tends to inhibit the stutterer's impulse or desire to speak.

larynx. The upper part of the air passage from the lungs which houses the vocal folds.

learned behavior. Any relatively permanent change in a person's behavior resulting from his reaction to or interaction with environmental influences or from reinforced practice; an acquired neuro-muscular, verbal, emotional, or other type of response to certain stimuli.

light contact. Loose or non-tensed contact of the lips and/or tongue on plosive sounds. Contact of the lips and/or tongue which is optimal for the production of speech sounds as contrasted to the hard, tense contact which is often a part of the stuttering pattern.

mirror observation practice. Self analysis through mirror study; practicing reading or speaking in front of a mirror so that the stutterer can observe his stuttering reactions so as to study ways of modifying or eliminating them.

modifying the stuttering pattern. Refers to the stutterer changing what he does when he stutters. Clinicians suggest that he can and should deliberately change his stuttering behavior and learn to stutter in different ways and usually in an easier manner. In so modifying his stuttering pattern he learns that he can change his way of speaking and that he can develop a style of talking which is less abnormal and free of excessive tensing.

monitoring. A technique in which the stutterer seeks to become highly aware of the articulatory movements of his speech, as well as other behaviors, which make up his characteristic and habitual pattern of stuttering. This would include continuous self-observation of the crutches and tricks he uses in his act of stuttering.

monotone. Voice characterized by little or no variation or pitch or loudness.

neurosis. A functional personality disorder, generally characterized by anxiety, obsessions or compulsions which are irrational but nevertheless real to the possessor, and which are probably caused by intrapsychic or interpersonal conflict.

nonavoidance therapy. Nonavoidance therapy is also referred to as avoidance-reduction therapy. The goals of this form of therapy are to reduce avoidance tendencies within the stutterer and to increase the approach tendencies. The first goal, reduction of avoidance tendencies and behaviors, however, usually receives the greater emphasis.

nonfluency. Refers to speech which is not smooth or fluent. All speakers talk nonfluently at times, i.e. they hesitate or stumble in varying degree. All stutterers are nonfluent but all nonfluency is not stuttering. For instance 'nonfluency' could be used to describe the developmental hesitations of a child learning to talk or the arrhythmic breaks in the normal speech of an adult, etc. Same as 'disfluency.'

objective attitude. Referring to the attitude that it is desirable for the stutterer to have toward his stuttering; a feeling relatively independent of one's personal prejudices or apprehensions and not distorted by shame or embarrassment; the aceptance of his stuttering as a problem rather than a curse.

onset. see "easy onset."

operant conditioning. A method of changing behavior which may be learned by controlling its consequences through reinforcement; any of a variety of procedures in which the experimenter or the clinician arranges for a stimulus to occur following the occurrence of a response. If the stimulus is a pleasant one, the response it follows will occur more often, but if the stimulus is a disagreeable one, the response it follows will occur less often. This process is often theorized to be the way in which voluntary behaviors are learned. Behaviorists consider this as the basic strategy for achieving behavior change. According to the basic principle of operant conditioning, stuttering behavior will occur more or less depending on the consequences it generates.

oscillation(s). In stuttering the tremorous vibrations or repetitions of speech muscle movements temporarily blocking speech; often used with 'fixation(s)'—see that word.

overt behavior. Clearly visible or audible stuttering behavior as opposed to 'covert.'

palate. The roof of the mouth; includes the anterior or front portion (hard palate) and posterior or rear portion (soft palate).

pantomime. In stuttering therapy a sequence of movements of the speech organs with no emission of sound.

parent counseling. Involves establishing a personalized relationship between the parent and a therapist to enable the latter to influence the home environment and particularly the feelings, habits, and policies of the parents as regards the child, so as to diminish anxiety—provoking environmental conditions as much as possible. Since parental atittudes can be the cause or part of the cause of a child's stuttering and a healthy emotional atmosphere in the home is desirable in stuttering therapy, wise and effective parental counseling is important.[1]

phonation. Vocalization; act or process of uttering voice; production of the voiced sounds of speech by means of vocal fold vibration.

pitch. Highness or lowness of sound depending on the relative vibration frequency of the voice.

---

[1]*First:* Make no issue of your child's repetitions and hesitations in speaking. *Second:* Eliminate or modify any conditions that tend to make your child speak with unusual amounts or kinds of repetitions and hesitations. *Third:* Do everything you can to make speaking rewarding or fun for your child. *Fourth:* Do everything you can to be a good listener for your child. *Fifth:* Do everything you can to make a speech a personal sharing for you and your child. (Wendell Johnson)

plosive. As a noun, any speech sound made by impounding the air stream momentarily until pressure has been developed and then suddenly releasing it, as in 'p' 'b' 't' 'd' 'k' or 'q'. As an adjective, designating the characteristic of a plosive, especially that phrase in which the air is held for a moment under pressure.

post-block correction. see page 115.

postponements. Stutterers frequently respond to the perception of impending difficulty in the utterance of a word by pausing before attempting it. To disguise this pause, they often use other words or sounds or retrials of previously spoken words.

pre-block correction. see page 123.

preparatory set. see page 123.

progressive relaxation. A technique for teaching an awareness of the state of tension in muscle groups throughout the body and an ability to bring about decreased tension when under stress. Some clinicians make use of this procedure to accomplish various objectives in stuttering therapy.

prolongation. The lengthening in time, or prolonging, of a speech sound or posture of the lips, tongue, or other parts of the speech mechanism, or a fricative such as the sound of the letter *s;* the stutterer may say "a—pple," prolonging the 'a' in apple, or he may say "b—a—by" for example, or "mmmother." Easy prolongation of the vowel sound on both feared and non-feared words is used quite extensively to modify the stuttering pattern. See 'modifying the stuttering pattern.'

proprioception. A general term used to cover both kinesthesia (the awareness of bodily movement and position) and taction (the sense of touch or contact). Speech apparently is monitored both through auditory and through proprioceptive feedback.

psychotherapy. The treatment of behavioral or emotional problems, such as stuttering, by counseling, or by re-education and influencing the person's mental approaches and his ways of thinking, or of evaluating his problems; any procedures intended to improve the condition of a person that are directed at a change in his mental approach to his problems, particularly his attitude toward himself and his environment.

Don't expect that psychotherapy will help your stuttering much. A psychiatrist or psychologist is trained to deal with emotional or neurotic problems. (Brown)

pull-out. Based on the hypothesis that it is possible for a stutterer to pull out of difficulty during a block, this term refers to a voluntarily controlled release from the stuttering block. (See "in-block correction.")

rate control. A technique in which the stutterer attempts to speak more slowly, often in a monotone with each syllable given equal stress, possibly in a chanting sing-song style.

regression or **relapse.** Having more speech difficulty usually as a result of reverting back to an earlier faulty manner of talking.

resonant. Having a pleasantly loud full quality, low pitched voice. Speaking with vocalizations that are fully relaxed, adequately loud and appropriately long.

secondary symptoms. The abnormal actions or movements exhibited by a stutterer in trying to talk. These include, but are not limited to eye blinks or closings, arm swinging, grimaces, head or body jerks, foot stompings, lip protrusions, clearing the throat, excessive use of 'uhs' or 'wells.' Actually *any* ways by which the stutterer characteristically and abnormally approaches a feared word or struggles to release himself from a movement of verbal inability.

slide. Uttering the different sounds of a syllable in a transitory slow motion often with prolongation of the vowel; sliding through a syllable on which stuttering is anticipated.

speech pathology. The science or study of disorders of speech, language and voice and their diagnosis and treatment.

stammering. Synonymous with 'stuttering.'

starter. Refers to any means or device which the stutterer has acquired as a means of 'breaking' a block in order to start the words he intends to say. These reactions can be any unnatural movement such as eye blinking, arm swimging, head jerking, clearing the throat, excessive use of "uhs," "wells," etc. This word recalls the popular notion that to "whistle" may help a person to say a word on which he is 'stuck.'

struggle behavior. This includes a wide range of behaviors performed by the stutterer in his attempts to force trouble-free speech while stuttering. It involves excessive effort or tension, noises added to the words, changes in pitch, secondary symptoms, etc.

stuttering. Stuttering is a communication disorder characterized by excessive involuntary disruptions or blockings in the flow of speech, particularly when such disruptions consist of repetitions or prolongations of a sound or syllable, and when they are accompanied by avoidance struggle behavior. To the adult stutterer it is usually the feeling of loss of control of the ability to move forward in speech automatically.

Note: Most speech pathologists frown on labeling the developmental hesitations of a child learning to talk as 'stuttering' when there are no avoidance or struggle reactions.

stuttering pattern. In the case of the individual stutterer, refers to the particular way he experiences difficulty in talking, or the specific things he does, and the order in which he does these things that interfere with his speaking; the particular sequence of reactions in his stuttering speech behavior.

tension. Mental, emotional or nervous strain, often resulting in unnecessary intensity disturbing the normal functioning of the organs of speech.

therapist, speech. A person professionally trained in the treatment of speech disorders. Also referred to as speech clinician, speech correctionist, remedial speech specialist, speech consultant, speech pathologist or logopedist.

therapy. The treatment of any clinically significant condition, such as stuttering; a program or method of instruction, supervised practice or counseling.

time pressure. At the moment the stutterer is expected to speak he often has an almost panicky feeling of haste of urgency. He feels he is under 'time pressure' and with no time to lose, and so he has a somewhat compulsive feeling that he must speak instantly without allowing time for deliberate and relaxed expression.

tremor. Tiny vibrations of the lips or jaw.

voluntary stuttering. In speech therapy refers to a manner of talking in which the stutterer in a conscoius way imitates a pattern of stuttering. Voluntary stuttering may take the form of easy prolongation, or relatively spontaneous and effortless repetition, of the first sound or syllable of a word or the word itself. This style of talking may be used as a deliberate replacement for the usual stuttering behavior and it is intended to reduce fear of difficulty by voluntary doing that which is dreaded. This conscious affectation of repetitions (or other forms of disfluency, including prolongations, hesitations, etc.) is also designed to eliminate other avoidance reactions.

vowel sound. A voiced speech sound in the articulation of which the oral part of the breath channel is not blocked and not constricted enough to cause audible friction; broadly, the most prominent sound in a syllable.

Authors of Quotations

★SOL ADLER, Ph.D.
Professor of Speech Pathology
University of Tennessee, Knoxville

★JOSEPH G. AGNELLO, Ph.D.
Professor of Speech Pathology
University of Cincinnati

MERLE ANSBERRY, Ph.D.
Professor Emeritus of Speech Pathology
University of Hawaii, Honolulu

✦JAMES T. ATEN, Ph.D.
Chairman of Speech Pathology Section
V. A. Hospital, Long Beach, California

★DOMINICK A. BARBARA, Ph.D., M.D.
Psychiatrist
Karen Horney Clinic, New York City

OLIVER BLOODSTEIN, Ph.D.
Professor of Speech Pathology
Brooklyn College, City University of New York

✦C. S. BLUEMEL, M.D.
*Late Fellow of the American Psychiatric Association
and the American College of Physicians*

★RICHARD M. BOEHMLER, Ph.D.
Professor of Speech Pathology
University of Montana, Missoula

★JOHN L. BOLAND, Ph.D.
Clinical Psychiatrist
Oklahoma Psychological and Educational Center, Oklahoma City

★SPENCER F. BROWN, Ph.D., M.D.
formerly Associate Professor of Pediatrics
University of Iowa, Iowa City

EDWARD G. CONTURE, Ph.D.
Associate Professor of Speech Pathology
Syracuse University, New York

✦PAUL R. CZUCHNA, M.A.
Director of Stuttering Programs
Western Michigan University, Kalamazoo

★LON L. EMERICK, Ph.D.
Professor of Speech Pathology
Northern Michigan University, Marquette

★Authorities who have been stutterers.

★ HENRY FREUND, M.D.
Fellow American Psychiatric Association
Milwaukee, Wisconsin

★ SCOTT GARLAND, M.D.
Occupational Medicine
Winston Salem, North Carolina

★ HUGO H. GREGORY, Ph.D.
Professor and Head, Speech and Language Pathology
Northwestern University, Evanston, Illinois

★ BARRY E. GUITAR, Ph.D.
Associate Professor Speech Pathology
University of Vermont, Burlington

★ GERALD F. JOHNSON, Ph.D.
Professor of Speech Pathology
University of Wisconsin, Stevens Point

★ WENDELL JOHNSON, Ph.D.
formerly Professor of Speech Pathology and
Director of Speech Clinic
University of Iowa, Iowa City

★ ALAN G. KAMHI, Ph.D.
Assistant Professor of Speech Pathology
Memphis State University, Memphis, Tennessee

★ GARY N. LaPORTE, M.A.
formerly Coordinator of Speech Pathology Programs
University of Tampa, Florida

★ HAROLD L. LUPER, Ph.D.
Professor and Head, Speech Pathology Department
University of Tennessee, Knoxville

★ FREDERICK MARTIN, M.D.
formerly Superintendent of Speech Corrections
New York City Schools

★ GERALD R. MOSES, Ph.D.
Associate Professor of Speech Pathology
Eastern Michigan University, Ypsilanti

★ FREDERICK P. MURRAY, Ph.D.
Director, Division of Speech Pathology
University of New Hampshire, Durham

★ MARGARET M. NEELY, Ph.D.
Director, Baton Rouge Speech and Hearing Foundation
Baton Rouge, Louisiana

WILLIAM H. PERKINS, Ph.D.
Director, Intensive Therapy Program for Stuttering
University of Southern California, Los Angeles

★Authorities who have been stutterers.

186

★THEODORE J. PETERS, Ph.D.
Professor of Speech Pathology
University of Wisconsin, Eau Claire

★MARGARET RAINEY, Ph.D.
Director, Speech Pathology
Shorewood Public Schools, Wisconsin

PETER ROSENBERGER, M.D.
Director, Learning Disorders Unit
Massachusetts General Hospital, Harvard Medical School, Boston

★JOSEPH G. SHEEHAN, Ph.D.
Professor of Psychology
University of California, Los Angeles

★HAROLD B. STARBUCK, Ph.D.
Distinguished Service Emeritus Professor Speech Pathology
State University College, Geneseo, New York

★COURTNEY STROMSTA, Ph.D.
Professor of Speech Pathology
Western Michigan University, Kalamazoo

★WILLIAM D. TROTTER, Ph.D.
Director, Communicative Disorders
Marquette University, Milwaukee

✷CHARLES VANRIPER, Ph.D.
Distinguished Professor Emeritus of Speech Pathology
Western Michigan University, Kalamazoo

✷CONRAD WEDBERG, M.A.
formerly Director of Speech Therapy
Alhambra City School, California

✷DEAN WILLIAMS, Ph.D.
Professor of Speech Pathology
University of Iowa, Iowa City

✷J. DAVID WILLIAMS, Ph.D.
Professor of Speech Pathology
Northern Illinois University, DeKalb

✷ Authorities who have been stutterers.

Most of the quotations used in this book came from the following publications: A Clinician's Guide to Stuttering; Sol Adler (Charles C. Thomas). Questions and Answers on Stuttering; Dominick A. Barbara (Charles C. Thomas). The Psychotherapy of Stuttering; Dominick A. Barbara, Ed. (Charles C. Thomas). The Riddle of Stuttering; C. S. Bluemel (Interstate Publishing). Stuttering, A Second Symposium; Jon Eisenson, Ed. (Harper & Row). An Analysis of Stuttering; Emerick and Hamre, Ed. (Interstate Publishing). Psychopathology and the Problems of Stuttering; Henry Freund (Charles C. Thomas). Controversies About Stuttering Therapy; Hugo Gregory, Ed. (University Park Press). Learning Theory and Stuttering Therapy; Hugo Gregory, Ed. (Northwestern University Press). People in Quandaries; Wendell Johnson (Harper & Brothers). Speech Handicapped School Children; Wendell Johnson, Ed. (Harper & Brothers). Stuttering in Children and Adults; Wendell Johnson, Ed. (Harper & Brothers). Stuttering and What You Can Do About It; Wendell Johnson (University of Minnesota Press). Speech Problems of Children; Wendell Johnson, Ed. (Grune & Stratton). A Stutterer's Story; Frederick Pemberton Murray (Interstate Printers and Publishers). Stuttering, Research and Therapy; Joseph Sheehan, Ed. (Harper & Brothers). Handbook of Speech Pathology; Lee Edward Travis, Ed. (Appleton-Century-Crofts). Speech Correction; Charles VanRiper (Prentice-Hall). The Nature of Stuttering; Charles VanRiper (Prentice-Hall). The Treatment of Stuttering; Charles Van Riper (Prentice-Hall). Speech Therapy, A Book of Readings; Charles VanRiper, Ed. (Prentice-Hall). The Stutterer Speaks; Conrad Wedberg (Expression Co.), and from the publications of the Speech Foundation of America.

INDEX

*If you feel that this book has helped you
and you wish to help the cause,
send a donation to*
Speech Foundation of America
P.O. Box 11749
Memphis, Tennessee 38111.

Contributions are tax deductible.

☆   ☆

The Speech Foundation of America
is a non-profit charitable organization
dedicated to the prevention and therapy
of stuttering.